MAN-MADE MEN

MAN-MADE MEN

OR,
WAS THAT YOUR LIVER
I SAW ON TV?

by Henry Still

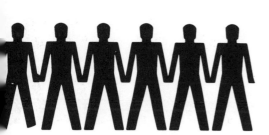

HAWTHORN BOOKS, INC.
Publishers/New York

MAN-MADE MEN

DESIGNED BY STAN DRATE

1   2   3   4   5   6   7   8   9   10

Contents

PART I

POTIONS, POWDERS, PENICILLIN, AND POT

1. The Elixir of Life   3
2. Drugs of Life   14
3. Out of Our Minds   31

PART II

REPAIRING THE HUMAN MACHINE

4. Rebuilding Flesh   51
5. The Body Shop   70
6. Artificial Men   90

PART III

KEYS TO THE KINGDOM

7. What Is Life?   109
8. The Core and the Code   122
9. Genetic Mistakes   136
10. Cancer   157
11. Planned Obsolescence   178

PART IV
THE PERFECTION OF MAN

12. Homo Novus   201
13. Serpent in Paradise   219

NOTES   231
BIBLIOGRAPHY   241
INDEX   243

PART I

Potions, Powders, Penicillin, and Pot

CHAPTER 1

The Elixir
of Life

On Easter Sunday, April 2, 1513, Juan Ponce de León landed on the shore of a land so warm and lovely that it might harbor the object of his long, restless exploration.[1] Since birth, he had heard legends in Europe of a magical spring flowing with water so pure that it would cleanse a man of all infirmities and restore him to youthful vigor. This was the fountain of youth, which offered the tantalizing hope of return to the Garden of Eden, from which Adam had fallen so long ago.

Ponce de León had sailed with Christopher Columbus and became governor of Puerto Rico in 1509. There he heard the European myth repeated by Indians. They told of the island of Bimini, where the water of life could be found.

In 1513 Ponce de León sailed with an expedition to find Bimini. He had passed the half-century mark of life and needed a cup of the precious water. All signs seemed right in April when he landed on the shore, which he named *Pascua florida* (flowery Easter). It was Christ's Resurrection day, and the subtropical luxuriance of Florida suggested it might be the lost Eden.

The explorer searched up and down the coast, tasting water from every stream and pool, but the fountain of youth eluded him. Eight years later he died in Cuba of battle wounds. His memory is marked only by a trickle of water at St. Augustine, Florida.

More than 450 years after Ponce de León, the fabled elixir of life surfaced again from the mists of antiquity—this time in Russia. In 1971 the Soviet Union reported the discovery of a powerful new wonder remedy that causes people to heal more quickly and kills bacteria faster than penicillin. It is called Siberian mountain oil (shades of the snake oil of the old American West) and according to Moscow's *Pravda*, is found "high on cliffs at the level of eagles' nests." It takes ten to twelve years to form, is from an unknown source, and comes in many colors.

Reportedly, it was tried on twelve patients, suffering from various ailments, at a hospital in the Siberian city of Krasnoyarsk. It was said that the patients recovered more quickly than others who received traditional treatment. A Moscow druggist, Alexander Mahkov, said natives of the Sayan Mountains have been using the oil for many years, though its wondrous properties have not yet been identified.

The discovery of Florida and Siberian mountain oil are two diverse milestones in the eternal quest for a panacea against the negative forces of time, which disintegrate the strength and sexual potency of youth and suffocate men's yearning for immortality. From primeval time we have prayed to stones, alchemists, magicians, witches, priests, the devil, and finally to God for potions to promote health and life, to deliver a lover and the power to love, and to provide the strength to extend our dominion over people and time.

Omnipotence escapes us, but we forget the millions of fragmentary increments of improvement which have been added chemically to our lives. Then we turn to agents of oblivion, the fermented grape and narcotic drugs, which offer momentary euphoria and ease physical and emotional anguish. The quest for vigorous immortality and escape from unendurable reality are two sides of the same coin. The quest is as old as imitative magic, a branch of the mistaken arts which predicated that the qualities of wood or stone, bird or beast, earth or sky, could be transmitted to or from humans by imitation.

By this ignorant short circuit of natural laws, primitive savages have eaten animals or plants to acquire their desirable qualities. (Slain enemies were devoured for the same reason.) The savage likewise avoided foods he considered harmful. A soldier, for example, did not eat the knee of an ox lest he become weak in the knees and unable to march. If he ate an animal that had been speared, he himself would die by the spear.

Ancient Hindus performed an elaborate magic ceremony to cure jaundice. The idea was to transfer the yellow skin color to normally yellow objects—such as birds or the sun—and restore a healthy color to the patient's skin.

Marcellus of Bordeaux, court physician to Theodosius I, a fourth-century Roman emperor, described a magical cure for a tumor. A root of sacred laurel, olive, or myrtle was tied around the patient's neck, with an end of the root left to dangle in the smoke of a fire. As the root withered, so should the tumor. The same Marcellus indicated that early teen-agers were as prone to pimples as modern-day youngsters who learn their cures from television. The physician suggested that a person troubled with blemishes should watch for a falling star. Then, while the star was still falling, he should wipe the pimples with a cloth. As the star streaked down the sky, the pimples should fall from his face. There is no record of the cures so accomplished.

Many early cultures venerated the strength and stability of stone. In Denmark the old men, when they were to choose a king and signify their deed would endure, cast their votes while standing on stones embedded in the ground. Special magic accompanied more precious stones, so it is likely that jewels were worn as magical amulets before they gained their later value as ornaments.

The Greeks recognized a milkstone that, when pulverized in mead and swallowed, produced an abundance of mother's milk. Such stones were used for the same purpose in Crete and Melos into the twentieth century. The Greeks also believed in a stone that cured snakebite if its powder was sprinkled on the wound. The wine-colored amethyst received its name, which means "not drunken," because it was supposed to keep its wearer sober.[2]

Primitive magic evolved into tangled skeins of false belief, but it also laid the groundwork for a power structure. The sorcerer often stood in a position of fear and power equal to or above the king's. From attribution of imitative powers from beast and stone, it was but a short step to cast spells by administering grotesque substances internally. If one drank a proper potion brewed by witch or magician, it might increase a man's sexual potency, cure disease, and lengthen life by warding off the evil spirits of illness and death. More often, it appears, spells were used to harm or destroy an enemy.

Magic's deep hold on the people during the Dark Ages brought it into bitter conflict with purer religion and the reawakenings of scientific thought. Of those years between Constantine and Columbus—A.D. 325 to 1492—historian Will Durant states that "rational studies had to fight for soil and air in a jungle of superstition, intolerance and fear. Amid famines, plagues and wars, men and women sought in occult forces some explanation of the unintelligible miseries of mankind, some magical power to control events, some mystical escape from a harsh reality. . . . All of these marvels remain deathless with us today, and one or another wins from almost every one of us some open or secret allegiance."[3]

During the confusion of shaping spurious supernatural forces into the concept of a single all-powerful God, men sought their destinies in the motion of stars. Demons lurked everywhere, notably in bed, where they were blamed for nocturnal emissions in men and untimely pregnancies among women. Every natural object was endowed with supernal powers, and the bishop of Cahora was burned at the stake in 1317 after confessing he had burned a wax image of Pope John XXII in the hope that the pope would suffer the fate of the effigy.

Alchemy, which had approached the method of scientific investigation before the fall of Rome, regressed to little more than occult manipulation of strange substances by witches and wizards. People swallowed "potable gold" guaranteed to cure anything. It was not such a panacea, but gold salts are prescribed to this day for treating some illnesses, including rheumatoid arthritis. Doctors still do not understand its specific action.

During the Middle Ages the fledgling art of medicine contended at every step with astrology, theology, and quackery. Thousands of Christians, believing in the divinity of kings, came to the rulers of France and England to be cured of scrofula by a touch of the royal hand. For the most part, however, the search for the elixir of life (or of death, including poisons for assassination) passed into the hands of witches. Their brewing arts were immortalized in the "double, double, toil and trouble; fire burn and cauldron bubble" of the three witches in Shakespeare's *Macbeth*. There, for our edification and to satisfy the bard's sense of humor, we are treated to a list of some substances that, when properly combined, could wield power over men. These range from a newt's eye and bat wool to goat gall and the fingers of a baby strangled at birth.

Because witches gained their power by consorting with the devil, their direct access to the source of sensualism and depravity brought great demand for potions to captivate a lover and increase sexual potency. Such potions often were brewed, by imitative magic, from objects that resembled the sexual organs (*vanilla* takes its name from the fact that its pod resembles the vagina). Likewise, powdered rhinoceros horn, because of the original's resemblance to the erect penis, is valued for male potency. Most clinicians believe the only power conferred is that of suggestion, but the rhinoceros today nears extinction because it is still hunted for its horn. The only aphrodisiacs that appear to have weathered scientific tests are cantharides (powder from pulverizing certain insects) and yohimbine, a crystalline substance from the bark of the yohimbe tree.

In the fourteenth and fifteenth centuries the church licensed the Inquisition to deal with witches as heretics, acting under a literal passage from Exodus: "Thou shalt not suffer a witch to live." Ways to detect witches were outlined by Jacob Sprenger, the Dominican inquisitor, who was genuinely frightened by the spread of sorcery. These maleficent women (said Sprenger), by stirring up some devilish brew in a caldron, or by other means, "can summon swarms of locusts or caterpillars to devour a harvest; they can make men impotent and women barren; they can dry up a woman's milk or bring abortion; by a look alone they can cause love or hatred, sickness and death. Some of them kidnap children, roast them and eat them. They can transform themselves and others into beasts."

Wondering why there seemed to be more female than male witches, Sprenger concluded it must be because women are more "lightheaded and sensual" and always had been favored instruments of Satan. He condemned many to the fire and set off a major witch-hunt for the church. In 1554 an officer of the Inquisition boasted that in the preceding 150 years the Holy Office had burned at least thirty thousand witches who, if left unpunished, would have brought the whole world to destruction. The witch hysteria occurred again as late as 1692 in Salem, Massachusetts, when nineteen women were hanged and one pressed to death for refusing to plead her case.

It was inevitable that among the thousands of incredible ingredients tried by magicians and witches, a few would prove to be truly beneficial—perhaps the juice from an aromatic leaf or earth mold accidentally included in a vegetable poultice for a wound. These things, through distillation of the ages, found their way into the annals of pharmacy.

Perhaps the most persistent thread in the tapestry of man's search for the elixir of life is the use of wine, liquor, and narcotic drugs. Since man began, these have provided exhilaration and temporary euphoria to mask, for fleeting moments, the pain of the real world. First taste of the fermented grape probably happened by accident, but drunkenness and revelry quickly became interwoven with god worship. This is not surprising if we consider how alcoholic beverages release the spirit and inhibitions; drinking led to sexual orgies and the planting of seed to win favor with the gods of fertility.[4]

The use of alcohol is linked with religion by an even older chain of apparent cause and effect. Men ate strong animals and parts of their slain enemies, believing their power would pass to them. From this it was but a short step in primitive logic to believe that if one ate the flesh and drank the blood of a god, the man might become all-powerful and immortal. Since gods could not be caught and eaten, their followers devised substitutes, such as the sacrifice of animals and humans.

One example of the contrived paths followed was the worship of Dionysus (the Roman Bacchus), best known as god of the vine and trees. The faithful believed Dionysus died a violent death (perhaps in winter) and was resurrected (with the awakening of growing things in spring). In one version he was hacked to death by Titans while he was in the shape of a bull. Worshipers celebrated his festival by imitating his death, literally tearing a live bull to pieces with their teeth in a drunken frenzy.

"They must have believed that they were eating the body and blood of the god," surmised Sir James Frazer in *The Golden Bough*, a classic study of magic and comparative religions. "The custom of tearing in pieces the bodies of animals and of men and then devouring them raw has been practiced as a religious rite by savages in modern times as well."[5]

The madness of bloody pagan rituals has been a prime target of Christianity since its inception. Thus the celebration of Christ's birth was superimposed upon the time of the Saturnalia, and the spring festival of Dionysus and other gods of fertility became the time of Christ's death and resurrection. When He instituted the Holy Eucharist, Jesus himself killed three pagan "birds" with one stone. First, He himself became the human sacrifice to God. Second, He allowed men to continue believing they could achieve immortality by eating the flesh and blood of their God (in the form of bread and wine). Third, He allowed indulgence of the grape to continue, albeit in moderation, by the consumption of bread and wine as His body and blood for the spiritual nourishment of man. In this way the heady stimulation found in wines and liquors became inextricably linked with the fabled elixir of life.

Similar religious ties exist with some mind-altering drugs such as marijuana (used 2,700 years before Christ) and mescaline, derived from the buttons of the peyote cactus plant in the New World. There is a major difference, however. Whereas wine and liquor are associated with carnal pleasures, the drug cults seem more oriented to the cerebral, a reaching-out to experience the mental power of God.

Peyotism was part of a religious ritual in Mexico and Central America in pre-Columbian days, and it exists today as a recognized religion among certain North American tribes.[6] When ground into powder and taken internally, the buttons from the peyote cactus produce physical and mental responses; visions and hallucinations may result. Before the sixteenth century, when Mexico was conquered by the Spanish, the drug apparently was used as a medicine and to obtain visions for supernatural revelation. The newer peyote religion developed during the second half of the nineteenth century. It became the most common indigenous Indian religion, extending from Canada to the Great Lakes to the Rocky Mountains in the United States. Combining Christian ethics and belief in the Holy Trinity, the peyote religion was incorporated in 1918 as the Native American Church.

Peyote plays two primary roles, according to its devotees. First, it opens the mind to visions believed to be direct communication with the Holy Spirit. Second, it serves as Holy Communion in the sense of devouring and incorporating the power of God. The Indians believe peyote was provided because God took pity on a poor, weak, helpless, and ignorant people. He thus made peyote and put some of His power into it to help the Indians. This help, which includes medicinal qualities, thus establishes peyote among the claimed "true" elixirs of life.

The element of seeking pity from the gods is an echo of the weak condition of man in all ages. He seeks a potion to transfer god power to himself. When it fails or only partially succeeds, he takes a larger dose, on the theory that if a little helps a little, more will help a lot. Eventually the connection with God is lost. The exhilaration and euphoria produced by wine, liquor, and drugs then become no more than temporary refuge from the mental and physical pains of life.

A case in point is opium and its derivatives, morphine and codeine.[7] Used medicinally and under proper supervision, these substances are good for subduing pain. Used habitually, the drugs induce a lethargic withdrawal from society. Studies show that in India, where opium is eaten, 50 percent of all addicts use it for relief from the pain of sickness, 20 percent for pleasure, and 30 percent for escape from difficulty and worry.

Except for an abortive American experiment with prohibition in the 1920's and 1930's, the consumption of alcohol for pleasure and oblivion has increased steadily. As a result, we live in a nation uncertain what to do about millions of alcoholics and others who spend more money on liquor than on food. In the 1800's the United States had a sizable population of middle-aged ladies who were opium addicts. Until the introduction of drug-control laws, these women regularly sipped patent medicines, such as Mrs. Winslow's Soothing Syrup and Pierce's Golden Medical Discovery, both of which were laced with opium and morphine. Many other patent medicines were based on a high percentage of alcohol.

Marijuana, another mood-altering drug, appeared in mixtures promoted as a cure for "all cases of consumption, bronchitis, asthma, catarrh, nervous debility, and all nervous complaints." Marijuana was not outlawed until 1937.[8] Coca-Cola, developed in 1885 by John S. Pemberton, originally contained small quantities of cocaine. The modern-day cola drinks no longer contain addicting narcotics, but under the prod of television advertising, a generation of young people guzzles soft drinks as though they indeed were life-giving elixirs.

It is among young people especially that we have seen a new and desperate search during the past ten years for substances that will ease the psychological pains of growing to adulthood in a world torn by conflict, greed, and hypocrisy. It is no accident that marijuana, LSD, and other narcotics and hallucinatory drugs have become symbols of the so-called hippie culture. In its more thoughtful aspect, this subculture aims toward a new religion of the natural world opposed to the mechanized society that has grown out of the Industrial Revolution. It will be fascinating to see if this new "religion" develops the trappings of a priest cult and borrows from old symbologies to press its war against older, apparently outmoded religions.

But the magic elixir to elevate men to supernatural power still eludes us by the sheer number of its fragments. As pointed out by Seymour Blaug, professor of pharmacy at the University of Iowa: "The proliferation of non-prescription drugs is turning drugstores into a wonderland." Five thousand preparations are now sold over the counter without a prescription, and no one really knows how to advise the gullible pill-popper that the potions he takes to increase energy or ease tensions may be poisonous and damaging in combination. "Anyone who listens to commercials or reads drug advertisements," commented Dr. Charles Winick, director of the American Social Health Association's program on drug dependence, "knows he can calm down, perk up, fall asleep, lose weight, and ease any number of pains and discomforts by taking one or another pill."

A case could be made that the magic and witchery of life

elixirs has simply moved from the Dark Ages to the television tube, but even in this day of instant worldwide communication, we are still tempted to believe in some magical substance to cure all ills and bring eternal life. One such hope is the cell-therapy technique developed in the 1930's by the late Dr. Paul Niehans, of Switzerland. Many wealthy and powerful people have traveled to his clinic to receive rejuvenation by treatment consisting primarily of injecting dried sheep cells into human buttocks, ostensibly to replace dying cells. According to a Niehans disciple, Dr. Peter M. Stephan, cell therapy in 1972 was being used in some twenty European clinics; the method, however, is not recognized by medical authorities or licensed in the United States.

Devotees of the procedure claim it not only conquers aging and prolongs life but also cures noninfectious ailments ranging from heart disease and mental retardation to acne, gout, sagging breasts, boredom, wrinkles, and depression. "We're even making headway with our research into cancer," said Dr. Stephan, "but we aren't ready yet to make any major disclosures about that." Among the late Dr. Niehans's clients was Pope Pius XII, whose devotion to the cell-therapy technique led him to appoint one of its practitioners to the Pontifical Academy of Science in 1955.[9]

The search for a single potion to ensure eternal youth will probably continue as long as men live to imagine it.

CHAPTER 2

Drugs
of Life

In 1928 a British bacteriologist, Alexander Fleming, was conducting research on influenza in his laboratory at the University of London. At one point he noticed that some spores of a common green mold had fallen on a culture plate containing staphylococcus, a family of bacteria which causes many infections. Fleming examined the plate to determine how the contamination had occurred.

To his surprise, he discovered that the mold, *Penicillium notatum*, had created a germ-free circle around itself. He turned to explore his find. Unwilling to accept accidental evidence of its germ-killing ability, Fleming cultured the mold in liquid and subjected more bacteria to the mixture. The extract stopped the growth of staph germs even when diluted eight hundred times. Fleming named his discovery penicillin, after the mold that produced it. The event was one of those unusual occurrences when a line of investigation yields happy though unexpected results.

It was not until a decade later that another research team, headed by Howard W. Florey at Oxford University, isolated penicillin in its pure form and tested it. Meanwhile, in Berlin, Ernst Boris Chain, a biochemist of Russian origin, had done extensive work in submerged mold fermentations, contributing a way to produce penicillin in useful quantities.

The synergistic work of these three men came at a time when a germicidal agent to kill infection was most needed. Thousands of men were suffering grievous wounds and infections in World War II. Many were saved by the new wonder drug, which came into common use after the war. A number of substances can kill bacteria, but most of these also kill some body cells. Penicillin kills germs selectively. In 1945 Fleming, Florey, and Chain shared the Nobel Prize in medicine for their work in opening the door to the age of antibiotics in healing.[1]

Discovering a therapeutic drug of great value in common mold was only one of many instances in which scientists found a grain of truth in the ancient chaff of superstition. There was some value in many home remedies and old wives' tales which survived passing generations. The extraction of penicillin could not have occurred until the scientific method had built on the many faltering steps men had taken before through devious pathways of ignorance.

Looking backward, there is a temptation to believe that progress occurs according to a master plan and timetable, that a great idea or notion cannot succeed until its time has come. Penicillin arrived when it was most needed, but it was neither the beginning nor the end of the quest for a panacea, a substance to cure all infirmities and rejuvenate mind and body. Even if we eliminate primitive magic, the trail of scientific search leads back at least to Aristotle in the fourth century B.C.

The foundations he laid in physics, biology, ethics, politics, and psychology dominated Western thinking for nearly two thousand years. His ideas became the foundation for the pseudoscience of alchemy, beginning in the third or fourth century A.D. and flourishing through the Middle Ages. Aristotle believed that the interaction of his "prime matter" and form gave rise to the four elements: fire, air, water, and earth. In theory, any substance could be changed into any other substance if the right conditions could be found.[2] From this grew the long, fruitless search for a process, an element, or a magic spell that could transmute base metals into gold.

Skilled artisans in Egypt combined practical experimentation with theories propounded by Greek scholars in Alexandria. From the beginning, alchemy was interwoven with astrological and religious theories and expressed in terms of perfection of the soul. Practitioners invented laboratory apparatus and assigned astrological powers of sun, moon, and planets to the metals with which they worked. While searching for the perfect reagent to make gold, the philosopher-alchemists believed that this essential purifier, once found, would also purify men, transmuting them to a state of vigor and health, perhaps immortality. As pointed out later by a pioneer psychologist, C. G. Jung, the symbolism of alchemy appealed to basic psychological tendencies. Men simply were striving for perfection without knowledge of practical chemistry. They thirsted for the flash of revelation which would make all things known and perfect.

The Chinese also practiced alchemy under the Taoist philosophy, which sought to illuminate the "way," or path, of nature. The combined work of both China and the West was used by the Arabians in the eighth and ninth centuries. The Chinese "medicine," which was a sought-for addition to base metals to produce gold, became the philosophers' stone of later European alchemy. It was believed that this stone could not only heal "sick" metals by converting them to gold but also act upon sick men as the elixir of life. Without awareness of their true value, the Arabic alchemists discovered new chemicals, such as the caustic alkalis, and improved technical methods.

Later, as the Western world emerged from the Dark Ages, alchemy moved back to Europe. In the twelfth and thirteenth centuries a few scholars, including Arnold of Villanova, Roger Bacon, and Albertus Magnus, set to work compiling scientific knowledge as it then existed. Alchemy enjoyed a vigorous rebirth, which finally dwindled under the light cast by the modern age of reason. Practical men turned to more useful pursuits than making gold.

One of these was Paracelsus, physician and alchemist, born in Switzerland in 1490.[3] (His real name was Theophrastus Bombastus von Hohenheim.) His work was based on the Neoplatonic philosophy that the life of man is inseparable from that of the universe. For him the biblical creation meant that the body of man is an extract of all beings previously created. Paracelsus introduced opium, mercury, lead, sulfur, iron, arsenic, and copper sulfate to medical practice. His lore was a mixture of lofty views, error, and superstition, but he founded the school of iatrochemistry, the chemistry of medicines, which was the forerunner of modern pharmacy. After Paracelsus, facts accumulated by the alchemists became the basis for modern chemistry.

We sometimes forget that this long travel, mostly down a wrong road, required more than one thousand years of human thought, but it was paralleled by the work of the physicians. These were healers who sensed an intrinsic truth: that manmade potions and drugs could not remake a man but only subdue the forces of disease—whether evil spirit, germ, or virus— so that man could heal himself. They applied purgatives and emetics, but most "medicine" consisted of herbs (few beneficial) and a number of disgusting substances designed to chase out evil spirits by revulsion.

Prescientific medicine attained high levels in ancient Egypt, where physicians were priests and sometimes were deified, as was Imhotep, who lived three thousand years before Christ. Among their drugs were honey, salt, cedar oil, copper sulfate, alum, brains, stag's horn, and oil of camomile. The Mesopotamian drug list of the time was even more sophisticated, containing hundreds of mineral and animal substances.

The name that stands above others at the dawn of medicine is Hippocrates. This legendary healer was born about 460 B.C. on the island of Kos near Asia Minor. He practiced in Thrace,

Thessaly, Delos, and Athens and died at an age between 85 and
110 (reports vary), leaving volumes of reports and clinical case
histories. The Hippocratic collection of early Greek medicine is
believed to have come not from one man but many, but healers
ever since have been guided by the Hippocratic Oath, one of
the highest ethical codes in history. It reads in part:

> The regimen I adopt shall be for the benefit of my patients ac-
> cording to my ability and judgment and not for their hurt or
> for any wrong. I will give no deadly drug to any, though it
> be asked of me, nor will I counsel such, and especially I will
> not aid a woman to procure abortion. Whatsoever house I
> enter, there will I go for the benefit of the sick, refraining from
> all wrongdoing or corruption. . . . Whatsoever things I see
> or hear concerning the life of men, which ought not to be
> noised abroad, I will keep in silence thereon, counting such
> things as sacred secrets.[4]

Aristotle's view of the four basic elements of earth dovetailed
with the Hippocratic belief that the body is composed of four
"humors," or liquids: blood, phlegm, black bile (melancholy),
and yellow bile (choler). Any imbalance of these humors, it
was thought, gave rise to sickness.

The Romans borrowed their medicine from the Greeks. One
well-known physician, Dioscorides, served in the army of Nero.
He established medical botany as an applied science. His *Materia Medica* details the properties of some six hundred medicinal plants and describes animal products of curative value.
The medical wisdom of Greece peaked again with Galen of
Pergamum in the second century A.D. He developed a physiological scheme that guided medical men for more than one
thousand years. Medieval medicine became little more than
adaptations and corruptions of the Galenic teachings.

The ages following the fall of Rome in the fifth century were
dark in many terrible ways. Europe seethed in corrupt political
and religious turmoil. Death for the common man lay at every
turning of day to night. Babies frequently did not survive birth.

Mothers died of infection. In the absence of consistent human leadership, the Western world was "ruled" by a mass of supernatural forces, particularly evil spirits inhaled with every breath.

If invading armies occasionally failed to destroy the people, disease did the work for them. The horror of unknown forces shriveled men's minds and bodies when the plague moved miasmatically across the land.[5] The great killer first struck in Europe in the sixth century, when a cycle of the plague lasted for fifty years and appeared intermittently through A.D. 690.

The feast for the rats, provided by people throughout medieval times, was primarily responsible for the control of human population. In the eleventh century the plague broke out in Germany six times and raged so violently that it appeared mankind might be obliterated.[6] It was in the fourteenth century, when the disease swept all of Europe, that the name Black Death came into common usage. It broke out first in England and by 1369 destroyed nearly one-half of the population. In all of Europe some twenty-five million died.

No one linked the scourge with polluted water. A few noted that many rats died before a plague began, but they were unable to link rats with fleas and fleas with the deadly germ they carried. People theorized the disease came from changes in the air, poisonous vapors, or clouds of invisible insects that were inhaled or eaten. The latter notion, finally a hint of the villainous microbes proliferating in filth, was still no more than an idea three centuries later in 1664–1665, when the plague again swept England. Deaths in London in 1665 numbered 68,596 out of a total population of about 460,000.

We forget how much has been done to lengthen the lives of men and that most improvements have come in the past one hundred years. In 1841 the average life-span in London was only thirty-six years. In Liverpool and Manchester it was twenty-six. Genuine control of the plague did not come until the day of immunization, sanitation, and germ-killing drugs. Researchers in Bombay in 1905 finally discovered the exact link between rats and fleas and the deadly germ that spreads accidentally to people. Even then the danger was not gone from much of the world, and as late as 1972 there were indications the plague was spreading again, borne on the wings of jet travel from Asia to Europe.

The plagues spurred new studies in medicine in the fifteenth and sixteenth centuries. Printing by movable type started the spread of information, and world explorers brought back new drugs from America. These included ipecac, used to induce vomiting and treat amoebic dysentery, and tobacco, used as a narcotic. They also included quinine, a bitter drug extracted from the bark of the cinchona tree, which grew on the east slope of the Andes. Quinine was used by South American Indians before the Spanish conquest in 1500. Since then it has served to reduce fevers and suppress malaria. It is still used against malaria in much of the world, though it has been replaced in the United States by synthetic drugs, including atabrine.

World exploration was accompanied by advances in botany and drug-testing, but magical cures persisted even then. The first edition of the London *Pharmacopoeia*, published in 1618, contained some 1,960 remedies, including worms, lozenges of dried vipers, fox lungs (for asthma), powders of precious stones, oil of brick, and oil of ants. Thirty years later new compounds included Gascoyne's powder. It was mixed of bezoar (a ball, formed in the stomach, of hair and other foreign accretions), amber, pearls, crabs' eyes, coral, and black tops of crab claws. In 1677 such things as cinchona bark, burnt alum, digitalis, and benzoin appeared for the first time. Recommended cures also included Irish whiskey and human urine.

Remedies for various illnesses included blood, parts and excreta of many animals, fur, feathers, hair, isinglass, human perspiration, spider webs, wood lice, and a piece of bone from the skull of an executed criminal. Oil of spiders and earthworms was prescribed for the plague. One "cure" for dysentery was cat ointment and oil of puppies boiled with earthworms.

Healers of the sixteenth and seventeenth centuries thus had many worthless substances to work with while more efficacious elements crept in. Scientific investigators were also beginning to sneak up on the germ. In 1546 Girolomo Fracastoro, of Verona, speculated that infectious disease was transferred from one person to another by the passage of minute bodies having the power of multiplication.

In 1590 Zacharias Jansen devised the first compound microscope, which gave later investigators, for the first time, the ability to see the cell structure of human tissue. It was not until early in the nineteenth century, however, that it was proved that certain diseases were associated with microorganisms (first named *animalculae*). This was the prime pivot point of medical history. It gave healers an accurate target, though a more devious and elusive one than anyone at the time imagined.

Though the plague was the most notorious killer, other communicable diseases, such as diphtheria, typhoid fever, and tuberculosis, threatened death at any moment. Smallpox, which killed millions and disfigured millions more, provided the key to prevention of disease. Medical observers had no inkling of the way the body builds antibodies to fight infection, but they had observed that persons who survived smallpox rarely caught it again. Edward Jenner, of England, remembering a popular belief that cowpox and smallpox were antagonistic to each other, experimented with the first inoculation. In 1796 he injected an eight-year-old boy with matter from cowpox vesicles on the hands of a milkmaid. Later the boy was inoculated with smallpox virus. He did not come down with the disease. Professional associates were cautious and critical of Jenner's work, but in 1803 the Royal Jennerian Society was established to spread vaccination to the poor. In eighteen months twelve thousand persons were inoculated. The annual death toll from smallpox fell from 2,018 to 622.

Jenner died in 1823, and his work was eventually taken up by Louis Pasteur, the French microbiologist who proved the germ theory of disease. Pasteur, born the year before Jenner died, worked many years before the germ theory grew out of his investigation of organisms responsible for fermentation of wine. In 1880 he was asked to help with the problem of chicken cholera, which was decimating French poultry. The inoculation material that he developed was for the first time named vaccine, from the Latin *vacca,* meaning "cow." In this way Pasteur paid homage to Jenner's use of cowpox to protect men against smallpox.[7] Vaccination is not applicable to many diseases, but Pasteur's successors have virtually eliminated a number of ancient killers, including diphtheria and typhoid.

Probably the greatest modern triumph was a vaccine for the crippling disease poliomyelitis. This illness is now rare in developed countries, but only a few years ago polio killed and crippled thousands each year. In the 1940's and 1950's parents dreaded this affliction, which could wither a child's limbs and leave him partially helpless for life. The polio vaccine was developed between 1951 and 1954 by Dr. Jonas E. Salk, then of the University of Pittsburgh. In one of the largest medical field trials in American history, 1,830,000 schoolchildren were initially inoculated. An oral vaccine was later developed by Albert Sabin, of the University of Cincinnati, who began testing it in 1955. Children in the United States are now almost completely protected against the disease.

By 1971 immunologists had achieved a vaccine against rubella, German measles. Although a common childhood disease, rubella was found to cause many birth defects when the disease afflicted pregnant women. Thus the new vaccine will help eliminate some birth defects.

In a strict sense, serums for inoculation are not drugs, but they exemplify how substances may be introduced into the body to induce it to build its own defenses. Vaccination we now take for granted, but through the years virtually no drugs existed that could kill invading bacteria without also damaging cells of human tissue. A few diseases, such as diphtheria, may be treated by injection of antitoxins. Arsenic, antimony, and mercury also have been used for a long time in treating some other diseases.

It was not until the introduction of sulfonamide drugs, however, and then the antibiotics, that chemicals of low toxicity were available for treating systemic bacterial infections. The sulfa drugs originated in the 1930's, when German chemists introduced Prontosil, originally a dye. When administered to mice infected with strep germs, Prontosil prevented death. After development in France, England, and the United States, the sulfas were used to treat battle-wound infections and some diseases, including certain types of pneumonia. Now the sulfa drugs are prescribed most widely against urinary infections, meningitis, dysentery, and other strep infections.

The antibiotic family, which began with Fleming's discovery of penicillin, is effective against many diseases, although the drugs do not influence virus infections and not all bacteria are susceptible. The sulfas and antibiotics have given medical men the power to control the venereal diseases gonorrhea and syphilis—if the diseased and carriers can be induced to have their infections treated sufficiently early. A general loosening of sexual mores in recent years has led to the epidemic spread of venereal disease, posing a major health problem in the 1970's.

This threat has impelled researchers to new explorations for vaccines against venereal infection. Meanwhile, new drug development also surges on in other fields. This is particularly true of the quest to control viruses, which resist the antibiotics. Here again serendipity, the happy accident, has played a role.

Nearly fifteen years ago Dr. Paul Gordon, a professor of microbiology at the University of Chicago Medical School, set out to find a drug that would improve memory and increase learning ability. What he found in 1971 was a promising control for a number of virus diseases. The drug is isoprinosine, a derivative of the chemical inosine, normally found in muscle tissue. Isoprinosine stimulates protein production by brain cells, but Dr. Gordon found it also prevents viral action by blocking the genetic information that viruses must carry into cells in order to reproduce themselves. Now approved for clinical use in Argentina, isoprinosine is being tested in the United States. In tissue-culture tests the new drug has proved effective against viruses that cause influenza, shingles, and chicken pox. It may also prove useful against other viruses.[8]

Most drug discovery, development, and testing is now a matter of expensive big business, but the stimulus to search may be as simple as an uncomfortable secretary. Such was the case of Mrs. Marilyn Rose, who suffered a stubborn case of boils on her eyelids in 1955 while working for Lederle Laboratories. Challenged by her problem, researchers isolated the bacteria from her boils and called the infection Staph Rose in honor of its donor.

Six years later, in 1961, Drs. James J. Boothe and Michael J. Martell synthesized a new drug, minocyclene, which protected mice against the infection. It required ten more years of testing and development of mass-production techniques before the drug was ready for human application. Lederle reported that development of this single drug cost seven million dollars in research and three million dollars for new facilities. The resulting drug not only cures boils but also is effective against shigella, which causes dysentery; pneumococcal pneumonia; typhus fever; lymphogranuloma, a contagious venereal disease; Rocky Mountain spotted fever; and *Vibrio comma*, the organism that causes cholera.[9]

Thus from centuries of search have come many drugs to improve and prolong human life. Not the least are those that subdue pain and make a sick person more comfortable. Many narcotics can block pain, but they are also addicting, and the cure sometimes proves worse than the original disease. Quinine was used as a pain-reliever until the 1800's, when a shortage sent chemists in search of a substitute. In 1853 Charles Gerhardt, a German chemist, discovered aspirin, a natural product of coal tar. Its medical value was not recognized until 1899, but since that time aspirin has probably been the most commonly used drug in the world to relieve pain and reduce fever.

Chemical insecticides probably have done as much as any drug or serum to improve the health and lives of people everywhere. By subduing disease-bearing insects—particularly the malarial mosquito—these pesticides, including DDT, which came into use in the 1940's, have lengthened the healthy lifespan of millions in underdeveloped nations. "I estimate that no less than five million lives have been saved and no less than 100 million serious illnesses prevented," stated Dr. Edward F. Knipling, of the U.S. Department of Agriculture, "through the use of DDT for controlling malaria, typhus, dysentery and many other diseases."[10]

It is impossible to catalog the thousands of substances (such as antihistamines to control allergies) developed within the past half-century to improve the human condition. Scientists have turned more attention to the balance of natural substances that sustain and regulate the normally functioning human body. Among these are vitamins and hormones, each of which has spawned its own field of scientific inquiry and application to human health.

Vitamins are specific organic compounds that exist in sufficient (though small) quantities in a well-balanced diet, but this knowledge is relatively new.

In 1535 the French explorer Jacques Cartier wintered with his men in what is now eastern Canada. Most of the men came down with scurvy, an affliction well known to early seafarers. When a ship went out for several months, often less than half of the men came home. An old sea chantey says: "Drink and the devil had done for the rest," but it was really scurvy that killed them.

Cartier was wise. He asked the local Indians what to do. They provided tea made out of the bark of a tree, and it cured the scurvy. We now know the tea provided vitamin C, which exists in abundance in citrus fruits. By the seventeenth century the British navy was requiring every sailor to drink a daily glass of lime juice. Their improved fitness gave the British considerable advantage in naval battles.

Vitamin A, discovered later in butter, was found to be needed for growth, general health, and prevention of eye disease.

Rickets is an illness that has deformed the bones of babies and small children from earliest times. The ancient Romans attributed it to playing on cold stone floors. The English blamed it on the fog. They were partly right, because the disease is caused by a deficiency of vitamin D, which is formed in the skin by exposure to sunlight. A clue to other sources was found early in the 1900's by Elmer McCollum, a chemist at the University of Wisconsin, when he learned that the Scotch kept their children from getting rickets by giving them cod-liver oil. Thus it was that millions of early-twentieth-century youngsters learned the unpleasant taste of cod-liver oil administered to strengthen them during long winter months of low sunshine. Only later did chemists learn to package the unpalatable oil in capsule form.

For centuries the scourge of the Orient was beriberi, a disease causing multiple neuritis, general debility, and painful rigidity of muscles. The staple diet of Orientals is polished rice. The clue to the cause of beriberi was found by Robert Williams, a son of missionaries in India. In 1910 a doctor showed him a bottle of syrup extracted from the rough exterior coatings polished off the surface of rice and told him it would cure beriberi.

Williams spent twenty-six years finding out why. After going through tons of rice polishings, in 1936 he and his brother Roger learned the chemical formula for the curative factor in whole grain. They named it thiamine, now also called vitamin B_1. It is often needed not only in the Orient but also in America, where much of the nutritional value has been removed from cereal foods and bread.[11]

As each piece of truth fit the growing pattern, the importance of vitamins became more apparent. Too little vitamin E has been known to induce muscular dystrophy in experimental animals. Vitamin K is an important presurgical tool because it promotes clotting of the blood. Vitamin B_2 (riboflavin) combines with B_1 to assist complex metabolic processes of the body. Nicotinic acid (niacin) prevents pellagra. Vitamin B_{12} cures pernicious anemia. This is not a complete list, but the presence of vitamins in the diet is now recognized as essential to good health. Doctors are also able to measure conditions that indicate deficiencies and can issue prescriptions to head off illness.

Many people now pop a daily vitamin pill as readily as drinking the morning cup of coffee. Although some doctors have accused Americans of overdoing their daily dosage, the role of vitamins becomes more important as evidence shows the lack of vital elements in many modern refined and artificial foods. Concern in this area is expressed by a resurgent, if faddish, turn to natural (so-called organic) foods. Vitamin supplements are most important to dieters attempting quick loss of fat.

Unlike vitamins, which must be taken into the body, hormones are vital chemical substances secreted by the ductless, or endocrine, glands.[12] These include the pituitary, thyroid, pancreas, adrenals, parathyroids, ovaries (in women), and testes (in men). As discovered in relatively recent years, the hormonal secretions pass into the bloodstream and influence the remote activities of cells, tissues, and organs of the body. If a gland secretes too much or too little of a particular hormone, serious disturbances result. As a direct corollary, the dynamic continuing study of hormonal complexities and actions gives practicing physicians the ability to regulate some of these substances artificially for the improvement of physical and mental performance.

Probably the best-known hormone is insulin, produced by the pancreas. A deficiency of insulin leads to sugar diabetes, which may be controlled by taking therapeutic doses of insulin obtained from sheep, cattle, and certain fish.

Epinephrine, or adrenaline, is produced by the adrenal glands. Its function is to prepare the body to meet an emergency. When adrenaline is secreted, the heart beats faster and the person breathes more rapidly. Muscles obtain greater strength to meet the emergency. Administered by doctors, adrenaline can ease an asthmatic attack, contract the muscles in artery walls to slow the flow of blood from a wound, and even start a heart that has stopped beating. Aldosterone, another extract from the adrenal glands, helps regulate body levels of salt and water. The adrenals also secrete cortisone, hydrocortisone, and ACTH, which have been labeled wonder drugs in the treatment of rheumatic arthritis, rheumatic fever, skin disease, and burns.

This is only a partial list of the known hormones, and each year the science of endocrinology contributes more knowledge to the way these essential glands control the body and mind. Many extracts may be administered as medicine to change physical functions. Sex hormones are used in modern birth-control techniques, ironically to curb an exploding world population resulting from the death-control measures provided by modern wonder drugs and insecticides. Proper use of sex hormones may also serve in certain instances to improve the sexual potency of men and prolong the youth and healthy drive of women in the menopause and beyond into old age, thus partially fulfilling two of the oldest desires of human beings.

Until recent years it was unknown how the hormones go about their myriad functions, but in 1971 Dr. Earl W. Sutherland, Jr., of Vanderbilt University, received the Nobel Prize for experimental work with cyclic adenyl acid—known as cyclic AMP. According to Dr. Sutherland, cyclic AMP is made in small amounts by all living tissue. In some cases it is the messenger link by which hormones work. In others it triggers hormones into action to control such bodily functions as growth, development, reproduction, and metabolism. Knowledge of its function leads to better understanding of diseases such as cholera and diabetes, which are caused by hormonal defects, and may provide new clues as to why normal cells go wild and multiply into cancer cells.[13]

Delving deeper into the extracts that control human function and longevity, scientists have discovered an entirely new family of beneficial agents related to the hormones but of different chemical structure. These are the prostaglandins. As with penicillin and isoprinosine, their discovery came partially by accident.

In the 1930's two gynecologists in New York City—Drs. Raphael Kurzrok and Charles C. Lieb—studying human semen and seminal tissue from animals, found that both contained substances of high physiological potency. By applying fresh semen to strips of uterine muscle from women who had undergone a hysterectomy, the researchers found that the seminal fluid caused the tissue either to relax (if the woman had previously borne children) or to contract (if the woman had been childless). At about the same time Maurice W. Goldblatt in England and Ulf S. von Euler in Sweden proved that seminal fluid could cause muscle tissue to contract and reduce blood pressure.

It was Von Euler who gave this mysterious new substance the name prostaglandin, believing it originated in the prostate gland. Actually it comes from the seminal vesicles, and later research has shown that prostaglandins are also produced in smaller quantities in other body tissue. More than a dozen have now been identified.

Little was learned about the chemistry and properties of this new family of highly potent extracts for more than twenty years because such tiny amounts are produced that they defied analysis. For example, a man normally synthesizes only about one-tenth of one milligram of two of the most important prostaglandins per day. Finally, by utilizing the new biochemical tools of gas chromotography, mass spectroscopy, and X-ray analysis, researchers determined that the prostaglandins are formed by a class of fatty acids that are important to the regulation of the membrane of tissue cells. This knowledge led to the laboratory synthesis of these materials and the discovery that they may be obtained from certain plants and a class of ocean coral found off the Florida coast.

Experimentation has demonstrated that one prostaglandin can lower blood pressure whereas another can increase it. Others regulate endocrine-gland secretion and thus affect many physiological functions. One prostaglandin is highly effective in inducing muscular contractions in the uterus. It thus becomes an important tool for assisting childbirth. Scientists also see it as a promising agent for abortion, by inducing menstruation, and thus helping to control population growth.

Medical application of synthetic prostaglandins is in its infancy, but many beneficial results are already apparent. One is the ability to relax muscles in the bronchial tubes and open airways to the lungs of asthmatic patients. Another is regulation of blood pressure. Nasal passages may be cleared by applying a prostaglandin to constrict blood vessels. Another may regulate metabolism by counteracting the effect of hormones. Prostaglandins may also influence the transmission of messages in the sympathetic nervous system.[14]

Thus the centuries-long search through thousands of substances has created seeming man-made miracles in the extension of human life and vigor. Even the philosophers' stone of old now exists in the nuclear reactor, in which gold is only one of many by-products of uranium fission to generate electric power. These by-products, in turn, have become valuable new devices to aid in the diagnosis and cure of other diseases, such as cancer.

The search goes on, even into the center of the human cell, but drug control of physical functions is only half of the story. Drug control of the mind is the other half.

CHAPTER 3

Out of
Our Minds

In London during the late sixteenth century if the common folk sought entertainment of a Sunday afternoon, they might travel down to Bishopsgate and see the menagerie at Bedlam. The inmates were not really animals. They were people—insane, mad, demented people—caged and chained in the confinement of Europe's first lunatic asylum. Started as St. Mary of Bethlehem Hospital in 1330, it was given to the city of London by King Henry VIII two centuries later. By then the name had been bastardized in the common language to Bedlam, and a poor soul condemned to its halls was known as a Tom o' Bedlam.[1]

This was the depository for the unfortunates whose minds had failed or who were possessed by demons, the belief that has left us the word "demented" and its derivatives. At Bedlam violent patients were chained in cages and tortured and beaten to keep them quiet. The nonviolent were confined to communal rooms, naked and filthy from their own urine and excrement. Night and day were filled with the cacophony of weeping, wailing, screaming, and demonic laughter. Here the effluvia of a semicivilized race leaped and cavorted, scratched unbearable itchings, defecated, urinated, and fornicated on public display. Sane people came to watch—the insensitive to laugh and the sensitive to study in horrified fascination the misery of those who had gone out of their minds.

The dread of losing the ability to think is more deeply ingrained in the human being than the fear of any physical disease, with the possible exception of cancer. Also, as with cancer, families of all times have tried to hide their insane with a feeling of shame as old as the ostracism of lepers. It is difficult to understand from this why the demented were placed on public display.

Curiosity draws us to the scene of disaster or cruelty. The motivation to watch may be as simple as a sense of relief that the watcher is not among the suffering. More likely the public exhibition of the insane—as well as executions—found its roots in older and blacker superstitions. Until late centuries no one had a better answer for the cause of mental illness than possession by evil spirits or demons. Sir James Frazer relates historic examples wherein an animal or human victim was banished periodically from the community in ritualistic expiation of the evil and sins of all.[2] Since demonic possession was the ultimate of evil, probably the English of Bedlam saw their confined and ostracized brethren as the symbolic removal of evil from the remainder of society.

This syndrome reaches a higher point in Christianity with the belief that Christ died to take upon himself, and atone for, all evil in the human race. The banishment of demons to a scapegoat is clearly shown in the Gospel of Mark, which relates how Jesus sent evil spirits from a man into a herd of swine.[3] Following the example of Christ, the Apostles and early disciples continued to heal those possessed of evil spirits. The ceremony of exorcism became a standard—though now rarely used—part of church ritual. (This does not intimate that the church believes devil-possession to be the cause of insanity or that it believes that demonic spirits do *not* exert evil or maddening influences upon certain people.)

Most mental illnesses, however, result from natural though deep-seated causes. These were not investigated scientifically until comparatively modern times, and to act "like one possessed" still describes a person who appears irrational. In the dark of night some people whistle through the cemetery to keep the spirits of the departed dead at bay.

It was a long road from the tortured souls of Bedlam to the day when insanity could be considered and treated as as illness. Until the 1800's madness of all forms was regarded as not only incurable but also a disgrace. The German doctor Johann Christian Reil, a pioneer student of the nerves and brain, wrote in 1803 in his *Rhapsodies* of the pitiable state of men, women, and children consigned to lingering death in insane asylums.

By then insanity was attributed to yellow and black bile or to the heat of dog days in summer. Symptoms such as exaggerated self-esteem, jealousy, envy, and self-abuse were regarded as *causes* of madness. There was no hope of recovery. Remedies were administered only to control violence. A person suffering from melancholy or depression was treated with opium pills. Camphor was prescribed for excited or hyperactive cases. A woman suffering from the uncontrolled itch of pruritis was sweated. As an echo remaining from old prescriptions to expel unclean spirits, the insane were given enemas or violent purgatives to make them defecate or vomit. Some doctors bled the thumbs and foreheads of patients; others prescribed head poultices of the blistering Spanish fly or of mustard.

Most treatment was brutal and harsh. A melancholy woman was cursed and douched with cold water as she lay in bed. If purgatives and emetics failed to control violence, patients were beaten and chained. A shy, self-conscious man was confined in a cold, damp cell, fed on hard bread, and treated as a criminal. The normal hospital diet—soup, warm beer, and a few vegetables—was tasteless and cheap. In rare cases quiet patients were assigned to tending geese or farmed out during the day as harvest hands.

The first attempts to treat the mad humanely were carried out at the Quaker retreat founded by William Tuks in 1794 at York, England. Four years later in France, moved by pity for the demented and their treatment, Philippe Pinel removed the chains from forty-nine insane patients at the Paris Asylum for Men. It was a bold move, condemned by many, and required consent from the French National Assembly.[4]

Virtually no age, including our own, can be proud of the way it treats its mentally ill. In early America some were auctioned off to farmers like beasts of burden. Some were driven out of town, others placed in local insane asylums. In the nineteenth century improvements were stimulated by Dorothea Lynde Dix, a crusading writer who became incensed by the condition of insane paupers. Her work led to some success in transferring responsibility from local almshouses to state institutions. Later, in our own century, the biography of Clifford W. Beers, who suffered through the brutal restraints and treatment of an asylum, served to spur a number of needed reforms.[5]

Crusades to improve mental institutions were paralleled by scientific advances in understanding various forms of mental incapacitation. Pioneering forces included Emil Kraepelin, of Germany, who in the late 1900's classified the forms of insanity and identified psychobiological causes for some of them. While he and others worked from the direction of anatomy and physiology, the studies in hypnotism by Franz Anton Mesmer in Paris led to the foundations in psychiatry laid by Sigmund Freud and C. G. Jung.[6] Such men finally lifted the cloak of evil spirits and bad humors and began understanding the root causes of mental deficiency, congenital insanity (caused by such things as syphilis), and deep personality disorders. Until the twentieth century, however, the only drugs applied to treat mental symptoms were hypnotic and sedative preparations that clouded the patient's consciousness and impaired his motor and perceptual abilities.

In the 1930's Manfred Sakel, of Vienna, introduced insulin-shock treatment. Used in schizophrenia and some other psychoses, insulin is given in large doses until the patient goes into a coma. After recovering from the shock, the insane patient sometimes improved. In the same decade electroconvulsive shock was attempted with patients suffering severe depression. Electric current was passed through the head. The patient became unconscious and suffered convulsions, not unlike an epileptic seizure. Sometimes it appeared that these methods were almost as brutal as the barbaric treatment of earlier days and the cure worse than the illness. With electric shock administered for several weeks the depression ultimately might be relieved, but the patient might also become confused and forgetful for months.

The great turning point in the use of drugs to remake the minds of men was discovery of the first true tranquilizers—reserpine and chlorpromazine—in the 1950's. These drugs and many similar compounds, some of which are still experimental, began a genuine revolution in the control of human behavior. Tranquilizers ease symptoms of anxiety and reduce agitation without disturbing basic consciousness. They relieve tension, hyperactivity, explosive outbursts, and destructive behavior. Tranquilizers have also helped to relieve delirium from overuse of alcohol, suicidal impulses, and some conditions resulting from brain damage.

Tranquilizers are not a cure, but they modify the behavior of the most disturbed patients and so ease the management of hospitalized men and women. Noisy, untidy, and crowded conditions that formerly pervaded the wards of every mental hospital have largely disappeared. Because of the quieting effects of tranquilizers, hospital staffs are able to devote more attention to other therapy. Patients have greater freedom to move around. Many are able to leave the hospital for long periods or permanently.[7] An almost immediate effect from using tranquilizers was a reduction in the numbers of people requiring confinement. From 1931 the number of mental patients in the

United States had increased from 355,000 to a peak of 632,000 in 1955. By 1961, after the introduction of tranquilizers, the number had dropped to 515,000.[8]

These drugs were not alone in the modern wave of chemical behavior control. Working with them were the barbiturates—barbital, phenobarbital, pentobarbital, and others—which induce sleep to ease the debilitation of insomnia and relieve convulsive disorders such as epilepsy. At the other extreme are the stimulant amphetamines, which induce profound psychic effects, including wakefulness and mental alertness, initiative and elevation of mood, greater confidence, euphoria or elation, less fatigue, and increased ability to concentrate. These stimulants are valuable in treating depression. They help wean alcoholics from the bottle and aid in cases of narcolepsy (the uncontrollable desire for sleep). The amphetamines, with other therapeutic agents, also relieve muscle rigidity in Parkinson's disease and the shaking palsy that results from brain inflammation. Widely hailed as wonder drugs, the stimulants also dull the appetite and in the recent past were widely prescribed with dieting to reduce overweight.[9]

While barbiturates and stimulants were finding their place in psychiatric practice, another marvelous substance was forthcoming. In 1947 the Swiss chemist Albert Hofmann discovered lysergic acid diethylamide (LSD). When swallowed in small quantities, LSD produces hallucinations, depersonalization, and thought disturbances similar to schizophrenia and paranoia, two dominant forms of insanity. Other hallucinating agents had included bufotenine and mescaline, but LSD was a synthetic substance that offered the hope of revealing answers to organic concepts of mental disorder. All behavioral drugs influence electrical activity of the brain. With their use, scientists could conduct hitherto-impossible studies in both the healthy and the unhealthy functions of the brain and nervous system.

This growing army of drugs in the hands of competent practitioners has brought tremendous benefit to the mentally and emotionally disturbed, but they also opened a Pandora's box. It was soon found that misuse of the drugs could produce evil commensurate with their good. From mental clinics the drugs spread outward in nonprescription and illicit form. An irritated or bored housewife found sleep in barbiturates and indolent peace of mind in tranquilizers, which also helped her husband cope with the tensions of freeway-driving and corporate one-upmanship. The amphetamines helped truck drivers remain alert for long hours of travel and the student to stay awake cramming for the next day's big examination. Finally, with the hallucinatory drugs, a person could experiment (as men have experimented with alcohol and other drugs for centuries) with literally going out of his mind to a higher (or lower) level of mental awareness or blank out unpleasant realities of the world.

Irritation could be reduced to calmness, and depression raised to elation. With hallucinogenic drugs it was theorized (and tested by such respected men as Aldous Huxley) that the creative powers of the mind could be stimulated to new levels. It was Huxley's *Brave New World* in the 1930's that introduced soma, a fictional euphoric drug that would render everyone calm and happy in a world five centuries from now. The age of euphomania, however, is already upon us.

We watch a generation of young people feasting at an illicit movable banquet of pills and powders to fit every mood. The older generation continues to drown its own sorrows in alcohol, taking pills to ease frustration and becoming psychologically addicted to barbiturates for the blessing of a few hours' sleep. More than 167,000,000 prescriptions are filled each year for stimulants, sedatives, and tranquilizers. Those uses are legal and administered with a physician's advice. There are estimates that 8,000,000,000 amphetamine stimulant pills are now produced annually in the nation, but that only 4,000,000,000 are supplied through legal channels.[10] Mental hospitals are beginning to fill with youngsters who have taken a bad LSD trip or are suffering from speed (methamphetamine) poisoning or heroin overdose. Drug-related suicides are multiplying.

While those problems are being resolved, tremendous good can be realized from the use of mood-altering substances, which continue to multiply as rapidly as they can be clinically tested. Each year witnesses the discovery of new drug effects or synergistic action resulting from their combination.

Tranquilizing and antidepressant drugs and aversion therapy, for example, were found in England to be effective in treating sexual perversions.[11] In another study the drug phenalzine sulfate, given for relief of depression in male patients, resulted in almost doubling the quantity of sperm production and strength. This finding is being followed to see how it may relate to questions of fertility.[12]

Some years before the stimulants became an abuse problem, it was proved that their use could upgrade performance of trained athletes. In 1959 tests were conducted with swimmers, runners, and weight throwers under the influence of amphetamine sulfate. Data from more than seven hundred performances showed the weight throwers performed 3 to 4 percent better than without the drug. Seventy-five percent of all the athletes performed 1 to 2 percent better than normal. The youths reported they felt "revved up," experiencing increased strength and endurance, mental elation, and friendliness.[13] The extent to which these drugs are used illicitly to influence the outcome of sporting events, especially professional sports, is not an issue here. Clinical studies have established a urine test that can detect the presence of seventy-four mood-altering drugs if their use is suspected.[14]

The important point is that psychiatrists, pharmacists, and physicians now have a deep and growing awareness of what many of these new drugs can do to the mind and behavior. Aside from abuse and addiction, these substances pose the unpleasant possibility that entire populations could be stimulated to elation and aggression or sedated to passivity at the whim of a government agency or master controller. Some experts believe that the current wave of drug abuse is already a long step in the direction of controlling the minds of a generation.

Dr. Andrew I. Malcolm, of Toronto, Canada, stated his belief that drugs, from marijuana to pills and heroin, are being used directly for the chemical conversion of the young to the hippie-yippie life-style. "These drugs," he said, "are a swift, efficient version of the techniques used by princes and priests for centuries to win human minds and souls." He pointed out that the chemicals produce the same altered states of consciousness caused by brainwashing, evangelism, primitive dance, trances, and fasting. "The use of psychoactive drugs for conversion," Dr. Malcolm added, "has now become the crucial element in the creation, diffusion, and persistence of the alienated life-style."[15]

Another case—and this within the so-called establishment—can be made with the amphetamines, one in particular. These stimulants were first described in medical literature in 1930, and by 1968 there were fifty-one amphetamine preparations on the market, some combined with sedatives, tranquilizers, or vitamins. One of these was Ritalin (methylphenidate-hydrochloride).

The white odorless powder was first marketed in 1952. It helped elderly patients complaining of lethargy, depression, or change-of-life symptoms. At the same time Ritalin was tested in the treatment of hyperactive children, a class of youngsters believed suffering from slight brain dysfunction. Such children indulge in a frenzy of activity and lack coordination, which inhibits their ability to write, read, talk, or sit still in school or at home. Although the drug stimulated adults (those past the age of adolescence), Ritalin had an opposite effect on children. A daily pill helped a hyperkinetic youngster control himself better, reduced his frenzied activity, and improved his behavior and performance.

The word spread quickly. Educators began referring to Ritalin and similar preparations as "behavior-modification drugs." Obviously, dosing children with such chemicals could greatly relieve the "kid problem" of both parents and teachers. In some areas, including Omaha, Nebraska, and the San Francisco Bay area of California, doctors began prescribing the "happy pill" for general use with many youngsters, not necessarily those with brain impairment but others who simply exhibited the boisterous spirits of normal children growing up.[16]

By 1972 it was estimated that 250,000 children were being dosed regularly with Ritalin. Dr. Leo E. Hollister, professor of medicine at Stanford University, told a Congressional subcommittee that up to 30 percent of all elementary-school children in one area of California may be receiving the drug to make them more manageable.

"That a mental disorder usually believed to be relatively uncommon should suddenly become a major affliction of childhood is a mystifying matter," he said. "The normal exuberance of childhood seems to be viewed as pathological. This is another instance of a disease being invented so that a drug can be used." He termed the general use of Ritalin to control obstreperous children "a cop-out by parents and teachers." One educator, Herbert Kohl, agreed with the doctor. "The advocates of Ritalin are the real drug danger," Kohl charged. "Their attitude is that we'll mold and control the children, and if that doesn't work, we'll dope them into submission."[17]

Aside from the fact that use of the drug might curb and distort the driving force of brilliant youngsters, the use of Ritalin on preteens could turn directly to drug addiction when the youngsters pass into adolescence and the effect becomes a stimulant. In Detroit authorities found cases in which teenagers ground Ritalin pills into powder, mixed it with water, and shot it intravenously with hypodermics. In Sweden this abuse led to the banning of Ritalin.[18]

From the Soviet Union, where we are conditioned to expect any coercive method to control and suppress the people, recent reports have filtered out concerning the mind alteration of political prisoners in special mental institutions. Mind-altering drugs allegedly used for the purpose include aminazine and haloperidol. One smuggled document dealt with the case of Vasily I. Chernyshov, arrested in March, 1970, for distributing anti-Soviet propaganda. "I am terribly afraid of torture," Chernyshov wrote in 1971, after he had been held prisoner more than a year, "but there is an even worse torture— meddling with my brain with chemical substances."

During an appeal before a panel of authorities, Chernyshov asked: "What are you treating me for? I am really not thinking in the same way as before." Tamara Anatolevna, a doctor, answered: "Can't you get it into your head that we couldn't care less how you think? The main thing for us is that you shouldn't think at all."[19]

While congratulating ourselves that we do not live under such totalitarian control, it is disturbing to be reminded that we are beginning to use the same methods on our imprisoned criminals. This fact was pointed out by two editors of the *Southern California Law Review* in 1972 after the California Supreme Court abolished the death penalty in the state. Roy G. Spece, Jr., and J. Anthony Kouba wrote that the court decision contains a provision that permits "innovative types of punishment whose purpose is the rehabilitation or reformation of criminal offenders. . . . The court's dictum is unsettling," the two said, "because of the probability that government officials, who no longer can eliminate prisoners by executing their bodies, will feel led to eliminate prisoners by executing their minds."

There is cause for such concern. In 1968 prisoners at the California Medical Facility at Vacaville were forcibly injected with a drug—succinylcholine chloride, or anectine—that induces a deathlike state of total paralysis. In 1971 several inmates at the Illinois Industrial School for Boys filed a suit alleging they were forcibly administered a major tranquilizing drug, thorazine. A man apprehended after a series of robberies in Pittsburgh recently agreed to a prefrontal lobotomy in lieu of a long jail sentence. Spece and Kouba warned that the full arsenal of behavior-control drugs may be used to alter men's minds:

> When government does not simply suppress speech but attempts to intrude drastically into one's mind with sophisticated psychological techniques it strikes at the core value of the First Amendment to the Constitution—mind freedom. If an individual does not have control of his mental life, all lesser rights become meaningless.
>
> Americans must prepare quickly to choose whether they will surrender their free will to the state. If they delay, their apparatus of choice may be confiscated and the freedom of selection lost forever.[20]

Such warnings should put us on our guard. In the meantime many psychotic conditions and brain-related illness may now be controlled or alleviated by new chemicals, such as L-dopa, which is proving beneficial in treating Parkinson's disease. Behavioral scientists are experimenting with a host of new compounds that may control mood, improve a person's ability to learn, and even enhance memory.

The International Chemical and Nuclear Corporation, of Los Angeles, reported tests on humans with a chemical compound, Ribaminol, which may improve memory. Dr. Alvin J. Glasky, director of research, told the American Psychiatric Association that laboratory studies with animals showed that memory and performance improved 50 to 100 percent under the influence of the drug.[21]

A number of drugs exert selective influence on learning ability. Stimulants, such as caffeine and amphetamine, and tranquilizers may help slow-learning children to read and solve problems. A Canadian study showed that use of thioridazine with mentally deficient children increased their concentration, aggressiveness, sociability, comprehension, and work interest and capacity. Using the same drug with fifty retarded children in Virginia caused thirty-four to have improved attention spans and reduced hyperactivity.[22] Amphetamines, desamyl, and meprobamate improve animal ability to learn how to avoid an unpleasant experience, such as electric shock. A French study with college students showed that amphetamines improved their perception and speed of learning, but not general intelligence and memory.[23]

Similar results have been shown with certain of the hallucinogenic drugs. One is a complex chemical, abbreviated as DOM or STP. Adult volunteers tested with it learned lists of words faster than others who were given a neutral preparation (a placebo).

As pointed out by a U.S. Public Health Service review of drug influence on learning, the stimulant amphetamines have received more attention than other substances "perhaps because this compound keeps alive the hope that human performance is subject to improvement." The report cautioned that the performance pill—one equally effective for all people —is still not in sight. Test performances are positive in some cases, negative in others.[24]

An example is magnesium pemoline, a drug widely tested for learning and memory in animals. After experiments with rats over a two-year period researchers found the drug increased response to various demands for activity. Whether or not it acts upon some general learning mechanism is still unknown. Testing on humans with magnesium pemoline has produced contradictory results. In one series of experiments amnesia patients were given varying doses of the drug to test recall, resumption of uncompleted tasks, verbal fluency, and attention and memory span. There were isolated instances of improved performances, but results were not conclusive.[25]

Magnesium pemoline is only one of many chemical preparations being examined for possible use in controlling healthy people as well as the mentally disturbed. Some drugs affect taste, smell, hearing, and judgment of time. One of these, preludin, caused a variety of effects when tested on schizophrenic patients in Sweden. One man showed great elation and clarity of thought, a feeling of invincibility, sharper perception of

color, taste, and odor, and a powerful desire for sexual intercourse. The researchers warned that these effects were so startling that strict precautions should be taken against allowing
the drug to fall into the hands of addicts. The feeling of
invincibility produced by the drug, they felt, could lead to an
upsurge in crime.[26]

This danger had already been stressed in relation to the amphetamines and other drugs that heighten aggression, especially in men. More than one hundred drugs, from LSD to
stimulants and tranquilizers, have been tested in the United
States to discover their varying properties of reducing or inten-
sifying aggression and hostile feelings.[27]

Looking to the future, with its promises and dangers, Desmond King-Hele, scientist at the Royal Aircraft Establishment
in England, commented:

> We may come to understand thoroughly the processes of
> memory and learning. When trained planarian worms are
> chopped up and fed to untrained specimens, the eaters ac-
> quire the skills of the eaten. Naive mice can derive similar
> benefits from being injected with extracts from the brains of
> trained rats. Shall we, too, have memories injected?
>
> Certainly we may expect to see drugs for curing all mental
> aberrations and producing any emotion. The prospect of a
> pill-powered population is distinctly depressing to most of us,
> but how could we object to a harmless happiness-drug like
> the soma of *Brave New World?* Some people are permanently
> cheerful now; why not everyone?[28]

Dr. Perry London, of the University of Southern California,
warns of the dangers inherent in the ability to control human
behavior. He believes such control on a mass basis is not only
technically possible but also inevitable. In his book *Behavior
Control* Dr. London warns of the enormous power that may
come from today's medical advances.

"There is an intrinsic ambiguity about behavior control," he
said. "Whether its implications are more ominous or more

promising to individuals and society depends on how it will be understood, prescribed, exploited and contained."[29]

Dr. Frank J. Ayd, Jr., associate editor of *Medical Counter-point* magazine, echoes the warning and criticizes "scientism" as the new cult replacing adherence to Judeo-Christian morality:

> Scientism promises utopia, a synthetic heaven on earth—made possible by chemical, biological and technological developments. To achieve this objective, scientists believe that many drugs must and will be developed.
>
> Among these are drugs which will curb human reproduction, new chemical aphrodisiacs, drugs to induce hibernation, to ease the pains of hunger, to combat boredom, to transport men to mystical heights, to raise intelligence to high levels and to increase longevity.
>
> No one wants to prevent progress, but science should not be allowed to forge ahead unsupervised simply on the justification advanced by many that what science can do, it must. On the contrary, as Sir Theodore Fox remarked to his fellow scientists: "We shall have to learn to refrain from doing things merely because we know how to do them."[30]

So as we move down the final third of the twentieth century, we see the prospect for:

• Enzyme-inhibiting drugs that may eradicate certain disabling mental depressions—or cripple the brain of a foe.

• Therapy that can turn underachieving students or delinquents into bookworms—or brainwash a television audience.

• Alteration of a tiny part of the brain that can restore peace to a tormented, violently insane man—or turn a legitimate rebel into a docile mouse.

• Manipulation of brain waves so that an entire television audience could be influenced to believe and respond to virtually any given set of suggestions.

The last of these, though still short of mass control, is already being practiced in a limited way. As early as 1964, psychological experimenters found, through electronic brain-wave measurement, that people can be trained to produce alpha brain rhythms that oscillate at about ten cycles per second. Such brain rhythm normally occurs when the eyes are closed and accompanies feelings of relaxation and serenity. In this state a person is also more receptive to deep meditation. By amplifying tiny electric impulses to show a person what is happening in his automatic nervous system—a process known as biofeedback—an individual may be trained to control automatic functions, including heart rate, blood pressure, or even glandular activity.

One of the pioneer experimental psychologists in this field is Dr. Neal E. Miller, of Rockefeller University. He has obtained almost phenomenal results using the biofeedback technique with trained laboratory animals. Rats have been taught to change the frequency of intestinal contractions, the filtration rate of their kidneys, the amount of blood flowing through their stomach walls, and blood pressure. In one case the training was so precise that a rat could be induced to blush with one ear while not with the other.

A thirty-three-year-old woman who suffered hypertension (abnormally high blood pressure) without an obvious cause was trained to raise or lower her blood pressure at will. The training consisted of monitoring her blood pressure continually and rewarding her—with a sound or light signal—whenever her blood pressure fluctuated in the desired direction.[31]

Not everyone may be susceptible to such training in the control of unconscious processes; however, a number of clinics are now teaching patients to control heart rate and blood pressure, to change skin temperature, and to relax certain muscles by producing alpha brain waves. This enables them to control, without drugs, such ailments as cardiac arrhythmias, insomnia, and migraine and tension headaches. At the Menninger Foundation in Topeka, Kansas, people have learned through biofeedback to prevent headaches by mentally altering the temperature and blood flow in their foreheads and hands.[32]

It is here that Western science begins to cross paths with

esoteric disciplines long practiced by religious mystics of the East. There is a striking similarity between biofeedback and yoga, for example. *Yoga* is a Sanskrit word for the school of philosophical Hinduism in which it is believed that union with Brahman, the absolute being, or world soul, can be achieved through mental and physical discipline. Yoga offers directions for suppressing internal body activity, including breathing. Mental activity is also suppressed until the individual arrives at a state of blissful, serene contemplation of Brahman.[33]

Yoga, as taught by Maharishi Mahesh Yogi, who influenced the Beatles for a time, has become one of the many fads indulged in by Western youths in their scattered efforts to achieve higher states of physical and mental awareness. The similarity between biofeedback and the transcendental meditation of yoga motivated Harvard University researchers to measure the physical and mental changes that occur during such intense meditation. Drs. Herbert Benson and R. Keith Wallace reported that subjects in the withdrawn trance of yoga showed a slower heart beat. Electrical resistance of the skin increased markedly, indicating that the person was relaxed. The subject's body produced smaller amounts of carbon dioxide, and brain alpha waves increased in intensity, another sign of relaxation. Less lactic acid was produced in the blood, another indication of reduced anxiety.[34]

Many students who have tried the biofeedback road to a greater sense of control and well-being report that it seems to eliminate the need for artificial crutches for mental stability. As a side benefit of the Harvard study, Dr. Benson surveyed 1,862 youthful drug-abusers who had also tried transcendental meditation for at least three months. In almost all cases, 19 out of 20, the young people reported that they had given up drugs because their subjective experience in meditation was superior to the effects produced by drugs. In this way both biofeedback and meditation may prove useful tools in curing drug addiction and alcoholism.

Above all, biofeedback and meditation appear to offer a way

to equip many people for better living in a technological world that tends to jangle the nerves and confuse mental processes. On the other side of the coin is the possibility that unscrupulous people in positions of power could misuse the emerging wealth of knowledge in behavior control. And some will ask, as they always have, how far we should go in trying to usurp God's function in shaping men's minds.

PART II

Repairing the Human Machine

CHAPTER 4

Rebuilding Flesh

A brief radio broadcast on December 3, 1967, in Cape Town, South Africa, signaled one of the most startling advances in the history of healing: "The first human-to-human heart transplant in history was done last night by a team of doctors at the Groote Schuur Hospital. . . ."

Listening to the radio that day was Dr. Christiaan Barnard, the surgeon who had performed the operation only a few hours before. He had no inkling of the storm of controversy about to break about him. His only thought was for his patient, Louis Washkansky, a fifty-five-year-old businessman who had escaped death by heart failure, infection, and diabetes.

In his chest throbbed a new heart taken from the broken body of twenty-four-year-old Denise Ann Darvall, who had suffered fatal injuries in an automobile accident. Washkansky lay in a tangle of wires and tubes, receiving life-sustaining drugs and fluids while his new heart falteringly took up its work. Not far away the heartless body of Miss Darvall lay awaiting burial. She had also donated a kidney for planting in another patient. By dying, she prolonged the life of two other people. Whether or not the heroic efforts to lengthen those lives were justified is still argued throughout the world. Dr. Barnard identified his driving force after delivering a baby who died of congenital heart failure:

> I was not responsible for his birth with a defective heart. He had entered the world that way—unable to live for more than an hour. Yet that was sufficient time for me to be responsible for him. He came to me asking for a new heart. I could not give it to him. He had asked for life from those of us who should have been able to give it to him. We had not. We were guilty—not only for this little boy but all the millions before him who had died in a similar way.[1]

It was this guilt as much as anything that drove Barnard through years of experimental surgery to the transplant for Washkansky. The doctor did not differ from thousands of others who had witnessed the final moments of dying heart patients, suffering the same agonies of frustration in their inability to avert death. The difference was that Barnard lived to see one of his dreams come true.

He also lived the nightmare of watching Louis Washkansky die, eighteen days after the historic transplant. Drugs and serums succeeded in preventing the man's system from rejecting the new foreign tissue, but they destroyed his ability to fight off infection, and he died of pneumonia.

The fact that he lived only eighteen days with his new heart (Barnard's second transplant patient lived almost two years) reopened old questions of how far the physician should go to extend life. The use of Denise Darvall's heart demanded new definitions of life and of the moment of death. These may never be universally agreed upon, but the dedicated doctor and surgeon will continue to do everything within his power to postpone the moment of the last breath, the last heartbeat, the last electrical pulse of a dying brain.

The earliest known surgical operation was trephining— drilling or cutting a hole in the skull.[2] The first instruments for the operation, such as the obsidian knives of Peru, were hard stone chipped to a keen edge. Archaeological evidence proves that trephining was widely practiced by Stone Age men, a common practice from Europe to Africa, South America, and Polynesia, despite the separation of cultures by oceans and continents. (Some tribes of Africa and Melanesia still practice it.[3]) The purpose of trephining was either to release evil spirits or to remove foreign objects, such as a fragment from an arrow or a spear. The pieces of removed skull (known as rondelles) were kept as magical amulets, perhaps worn as pendants to ward off return of the painful evil. It is difficult to imagine a priest or a witch doctor opening a human skull in a jungle teeming with infectious bacteria: Death was almost certain.

Skull surgery was not the only practice known by primitive people. From the beginning of civilization the repair of soldiers injured in battle has held top priority. Early men dressed wounds with moss, fresh leaves, ashes, or natural balsams. Poison was removed by suction, and decaying flesh was burned away. A free-bleeding wound suggested bloodletting as a cure-all, and it became standard treatment through many centuries. An abscess was opened with a sharp root or thorn. Neolithic stone saws imitated the teeth of animals. Splints were used to support broken bones, and some prehistoric remains show signs of amputation. Crude anesthetics were alcohol and opiates.

The first instruments of bone and stone were replaced when men learned to use metals in the Bronze and Iron ages (1500 to 400 B.C.). The real beginnings of European culture were revealed by the metal implements found in the Swiss Lake Dwellings at La Tene in 1853. Before the La Tene culture, which dated from about 500 B.C., surgical instruments and techniques had been developed by the ancient Egyptians and Mesopotamians. In old Babylon the physician was covered by the law of an eye for an eye, a tooth for a tooth. If he caused a patient to lose his life or his eye, the doctor's hands were cut off. No one knows how many physicians practiced their art without hands or what inhibitions this law placed upon the practice of surgery.

Hebrew medicine centered upon hygiene and religious law regulating purity of food and prevention of disease. Through examination of slaughtered meat the Hebrews gained more knowledge of anatomy and internal disease than other contemporary cultures. Although they guided the world in hygiene, the high mark of surgical excellence was reached in India. Sacred books of the Hindus describe 121 different operating instruments. Surgical blades were sharp enough to split a hair and were kept clean in flannel wrapping. The Hindus apparently knew every important surgical procedure of the time, except for the ligature to tie off severed blood vessels. They also were excellent teachers.

Realizing the need for rapid, precise incisions without anesthetic, students practiced on plants. Hollow stalks of water lilies or veins of large leaves were punctured and lanced. To learn how to drain off excess fluid in an organ, fledgling surgeons practiced with cucumbers, soft fruits, or leather bags filled with water.[4]

In China religious conviction forbade drawing blood or mutilating the body, so it is mystifying that the one operation performed by early Chinese surgeons was castration. It was probably this natural aversion to cutting into the human torso that guided Chinese surgeons to acupuncture, a technique of probing needles into major nerve centers. Originally it was used for treatment of such ailments as gout or rheumatism, and Western scientists long ignored the procedure. President Richard Nixon's historic visit to China in 1972, however, revealed that modern Chinese surgeons have developed highly effective operating methods combining acupuncture with Western techniques.

Reporters who accompanied the President were astonished to witness the use of acupuncture in place of standard anesthetics in serious surgical cases. With needles inserted into key nerve points and vibrated, the patients remained conscious and without pain through operations, including the removal of a thyroid tumor and the cesarean delivery of a baby. Chinese doctors also report that acupuncture has been used successfully in treatment of mental illness.[5]

The scattered mass of knowledge accumulated like grains of sand through the ages in Egypt, Sumeria, and the Orient and came to a focus in the high civilization of ancient Greece. Much symbology of the medical arts came from there, including the legendary Aesculapius and the sacred serpent entwined around a rod.

The first military and naval surgeons, noted in Homer's *Iliad*, may have been two sons of Aesculapius—Machaon and Podalirius. Both commanded thirty ships and were described as "good physicians both." In the fourth iliad Machaon is summoned to remove an arrow which has driven through the belt of Menelaus, King of Sparta. He arrives to find the fallen hero surrounded by warriors:

> Instantly thereupon he extracted the arrow from the well-fitted belt. But while it was being extracted, the sharp barbs were broken. Then he loosed the belt and the girdle beneath, and the plated belt which brass workers had forged. But when he perceived the wound, where the bitter shaft had fallen, having sucked out the blood, he skillfully sprinkled on it soothing remedies, which benevolent Chiron had formerly given to his father.[6]

Hippocrates collated the old lore into a rational system and set the ethical tone for succeeding generations. Although he believed most strongly in assisting human flesh to heal itself, the Hippocratic collection also contains treatises on wounds of the head, fractures, and dislocations.[7]

Aristotle laid the true foundations of anatomy, which he taught by dissecting animals. (He believed that the brain was a gland secreting cold humors to prevent overheating of the body by the fiery heart.) First to dissect the human body were the anatomists Herophilus and Erasistratus, who taught at Alexandria during the fourth century B.C. These men identified the function of many vital organs, but they did not understand circulation. They believed blood vessels were filled with air. Greek surgery and medicine moved to Rome during the centuries of Empire, and the greatest Greek physician after Hippocrates was Galen, two centuries after Christ. He left writings of anatomy, physiology, and medicine which dominated the healing arts for a thousand years.

While rebuilding bodies was focused upon supporting conquest and battle, women were left much to themselves in bringing new life into the world. The midwife is among the most ancient of professional figures, and history reeks with horror stories of methods used to induce birth in difficult labor, usually fatal for both mother and child. The first authority on gynecology and obstetrics was Soranus of Ephesus, second century A.D., and he was the last for fifteen hundred years.

During those centuries millions of mothers and babies died through crude practices and infection. A woman in normal labor had only a fifty-fifty chance of recovery. In difficult labor she was likely to be maimed by a midwife or vagabond "surgeon." It was not until 1580 that a law was passed in Germany prohibiting shepherds and herdsmen from attending obstetric cases. Infant mortality was high due to bad hygiene. Cities had no drainage. Floors were strewn with rushes infested with vermin, and cesspools were sinks of filth and infection. All that can be said of this black age was that it insured survival of only the very fittest. The population of Europe increased hardly at all.[8]

In Restoration England almost half the children born were soon killed by disease. In the hot summers of 1669–1671 two thousand babies died of diarrhea in ten weeks. London's population had swarmed to seaside communities, living in filthy overcrowded tenements. Newborn children were salted (according to the old Galenic teaching), encased in tight swaddling clothes, and allowed no exercise. Eczema and discharges from unwashed ears were accepted as natural. The children of royalty fared little better than the poor. Queen Anne of England, who died in 1714, gave birth to seventeen children. The only one who survived infancy died at àge eleven.

Even after the discovery of antiseptics the mortality of infants and mothers remained high because most children were born at home, where cleanliness could not be ensured. As late as 1870 the infant death rate in England was 150 per 1,000 live births. In the United States infant deaths totaled 60 per 1,000 births as late as 1934. The rate was gradually reduced to 20 per 1,000 in 1970.[9] This dramatic decrease in infant mortality is mainly responsible for increasing average life expectancy in the Western world to about seventy years.

Knowledge of the body's interior developed slowly. Andreas Vesalius, of Padua, who died in 1564, published *De Fabrica Humani Corporia,* a great anatomical work beautifully illustrated by a student of Titian. It refuted the faulty descriptions of Galen which had guided physicians for a millennium. So radical was his break with the past that Vesalius was criticized and ostracized by many of his contemporaries.

His work was eventually vindicated and used by Ambroise Pare from 1510 to 1590. Pare contributed to the well-being of pregnant women and their children and was known for his army surgery and treatment of the new class of war injuries— gunshot wounds. He was a master of amputation and did away with one of the tricks of the wandering "surgeon" of his day, that of treating hernia by castrating the patient. The first "modern" cesarean section was performed in 1500 by Jacob Nufer (whose profession was gelding hogs) on his own wife. She bore other children and lived to age seventy-seven.[10]

The towering figure of the eighteenth century was the Scotsman John Hunter, who elevated surgery from a fumbling technique to a science grounded in physiology and pathology. Along with Giovanni Battista Morgagni in Italy, Hunter identified the fact that particular maladies were centered in specific organs of the body. They saw that removal of a diseased organ, if it could be done without killing the patient, might extend a man's life.

Two great handicaps had blocked effective surgical efforts.

First, cutting the flesh caused such pain that the operation had to be done quickly. There was never enough time to do a proper job. Second, if the patient did not bleed to death on the table, infection was almost certain to kill him. Resolution of these problems has come only in the past 150 years. The first successful anesthetic was nitrous oxide, or "laughing gas," demonstrated by the American dentist Horace Wells in 1844. It was followed by ether and chloroform.

In the same period Louis Pasteur's verification of the bacterial cause of infection was put to work by the English surgeon Joseph Lister, who recognized that microbes swarming in the air must be prevented from reaching the wound. He experimented with a number of chemicals and chose carbolic acid, which he sprayed in the operating room before surgery. After operating he dressed the wound with gauze drenched with carbolic acid, liquid resin, and paraffin. Before antisepsis, Lister had lost 45 percent of his amputation cases. Now the death rate fell to 15 percent.[11]

In view of animal and human experimentation through the ages, it is mystifying that the most basic function—the heart and circulation system—remained a mystery. It was left to William Harvey, who studied at Padua from 1599 to 1603, to put the pieces of the puzzle together. Galen had believed the arterial and venous systems were closed and separate. Harvey demonstrated that the heart is a muscular pump which moves the blood in continuous circulation. However, he did not perceive that blood receives oxygen in the lungs; he thought the function of respiration was to cool the blood.[12]

The door to the heart, however, did not really open until the twentieth century. In 1904 a German pathologist described rheumatic fever, which damages heart valves or muscle. Maude Abbott, of Canada, classified congenital heart disease. America's James B. Herrick diagnosed coronary thrombosis and heart disease resulting from hardening of the arteries. Successful surgery for congenital heart disease was performed in 1939, and two American surgeons devised the first operation for blue babies in 1945. A host of successful heart procedures followed.

These remained among the most difficult of operations because of the short time available to work on an organ that could not stop pumping blood to the body. This time margin was increased by two important developments. In 1953 Dr. Henry Swan, of Denver, showed that lowering body temperature slows blood circulation and provides a "dry" heart during surgery. A greater assist came with development of the heart-lung machine, which circulates and purifies blood bypassed from the patient's heart.

Heart and circulatory disease increased in importance as death from other causes diminished in the wake of new drugs and medical skill. More people now live to the age when vital organs fail from long use. The human heart beats nearly two billion times in fifty years. More than half of all deaths in the United States, 921,000 out of 1,700,000 a year, now result from disease of the heart and circulation system.[13] This is why so much attention is focused on the heart. Whether the world was ready for Barnard's breakthrough is another question.

A flurry of heart transplants followed his operation. The first in America was done by Dr. Norman E. Shumway, of Stanford University, whose work had been vital in setting the stage for the procedure. Other famed surgeons all over the world, men who had been poised at the threshold of this radical surgery, now tried it. The need was great. Each year 32,000 American cardiac patients cling precariously to life. Each needs a new heart.

By 1972, 174 operations had been done on 171 patients, with a high of 77 cases in 1968. From December, 1970, to May, 1971, only 6 such surgeries were performed. Caution was beginning to replace blind optimism. Many patients died from overwhelming rejection assaults. Seven patients had lived for more than two and a half years and twelve for more than two years.[14]

Early excitement slowed down because too many questions

remained unanswered. One is the problem of finding donors to match the tissue of waiting patients. A second is the ethical question of whether a donor is really dead if his heart is able to resume work in a new body.

The patient, however, does not question. Any life is the good life, and doctors cannot end their quest for ways to repair the human being. Dr. Shumway at Stanford pointed out that heart transplants are still in the "clinical investigation" stage. The same is true with transplanting several other vital organs, such as the lungs, liver, and pancreas.

The kidney, on the other hand, illustrates how a rare and risky operation becomes commonplace through practice. Until recent years severe kidney infection doomed a person to death by poisoning. Surgeons then learned how to remove a diseased kidney. If the other was healthy, the patient could live with only one. Other patients have been kept alive—at enormous expense—by using an artificial filtering device, the so-called artificial kidney. Then, in the early 1960's the first kidney transplant was done. By 1965, 392 kidney transplants had been reported, and 147 patients had lived for more than a year. The kidney transplant has since become a common procedure. Successful cases now number in the thousands.

As for other vital organs, surgeons have been transplanting eye corneas for many years. The first liver transplant was reported in 1965, though the recipient lived only a month. The first lung transplant was done in June, 1963, at the University of Mississippi. The fifty-six-year-old lung-cancer patient lived for eighteen days.[15]

In California a fifteen-month-old boy suffered from a rare ailment, Swiss agammaglobulinemia, which makes a person unable to resist infection. Doctors at U.C.L.A. Hospital transplanted bone marrow from his thirteen-year-old sister. Afterward the boy was able to resist a virus infection, evidence that the transplant had succeeded.[16]

Other examples of surgery to enhance length and beauty of life range from grafting hair on a bald pate to plastic surgery to remake a woman's face or bosom. The laser may be used to make infinitely small repairs, and techniques now exist to reach into, and alter, the human cell itself.

Procedures have also been devised to assist the heart, short of transplanting. One is "replumbing" by transferring veins from a patient's thigh to replace or bypass arteries clogged by a buildup of fatty deposits (atherosclerosis), like minerals in a water pipe, leading to heart disease and failure. About 25,000 such operations are now performed each year in the United States.

Medical experimenters believe that eventually thousands of people will be given new life through transplantation of virtually all the vital organs. Some doctors have transplanted nerve segments, and it may become possible to transfer some brain tissue from one person to another.

The gravest problem, however, is that of controlling the body's own defense department. Shaped by never-repeated miracles of natural selection, each man is like no other who is or ever was. It is also true that each organism in nature feeds upon another. The pattern of war and defense was thus established long ago out of the natural law that says thou shalt eat but strive not to be eaten.

In learning to ward off beasts and bacteria the body is taught to resist any substance unlike itself. The invader may be a killer virus; it may be an organ transplanted from another person or animal. Internal soldiers have been trained to repel invaders. They have not been informed that replacement of a vital organ may save their host's life. Thus the body's own defense system remains one of the two great barriers to widespread extension of human life by replacing livers, lungs, kidneys, and hearts. The other barrier is the shortage of spare parts in the right place at the right time.

The defense begins with fortification of the skin to repel traditional enemies—bacteria and poisons. Nose hair filters out some airborne invaders. Others are captured in mucus and eliminated. Stomach acid kills some microorganisms and slows others. Bile from the liver retards germ growth in the upper intestine. Outer defenses also include lysozyme, a substance contained in tears, nasal secretion, and other tissues, which helps kill bacteria.

If an invader breaks through the outer barriers, the first standing army goes to work. This is a brigade of special cells known as phagocytes. Stationed in the lining of body cavities, they kill and devour the enemy. The second standing army is made up of leucocytes, white or colorless cells which flow continuously in the blood to every remote location of the body. These number five thousand to ten thousand in a cubic millimeter (about one for every six hundred red blood cells) in three classes: granulocytes, monocytes, and lymphocytes. They are formed in bone marrow, spleen, and lymph glands and cooperate to produce and carry the actual antibodies that destroy or neutralize attackers. The classical object is to pin down the enemy and fight a local battle, but if the invaders are too strong, infection spreads, and the body may need help from outside, such as a dose of antibiotics.[17]

If leucocytes are soldiers, their weapons are antibodies in the blood serum. These are immunoglobulins, built of protein, which is a vital ingredient of all body cells. But viruses and bacteria also are made of protein. So the body's fight against infection or alien tissue comes down to one form of protein battling another. It is war at the molecular level. Most marvelous is the fact that the defense recognizes friend or foe, identifies the exact nature of the enemy (such as the difference between smallpox and measles), and then conducts the appropriate war—all without conscious direction from the brain.

Ever since discovery of smallpox vaccine, investigators have understood that the internal armies form a general defense but also are specific in action. Inoculating a person against one microorganism, such as diphtheria, causes specific antibodies to build up against the disease. A person is naturally immune to some diseases and immune to others after having suffered them. The training school for production of specific antibodies apparently lies in the thymus gland, which, at birth, contains lymphocytic precursors which program the immunologic capabilities of the body for the remainder of one's life.[18] Isolation of gamma globulin as the center of antibody activity in blood serum led to the ability to inject the pure substance to help an individual ward off a specific disease.

Researchers can now see into molecules so tiny that thousands can fit in an inch, and the molecule itself is made of smaller pieces. In 1969 Gerald M. Edelman at Rockefeller University deciphered the sequence of components in one protein molecule of gamma globulin, the molecule of immunity. It consisted of 1,320 amino acids containing 19,996 individual atoms, and this is a relatively simple protein.[19]

In 1971 Dr. Lee Simon, of the Institute for Cancer Research in Philadelphia, took electron microphotos that show how bacteriophages (bacteria eaters) actually attach themselves to a germ, infect it by squirting DNA (deoxyribonucleic acid) through a minuscule syringe, and then enter to devour the germ. So tiny are these germ-destroyers that they are measured in angstroms (1/10,000,000,000 of a meter).[20] As Jonathan Swift wrote at the beginning of the eighteenth century:

> So naturalists observe, a flea
> Hath smaller fleas that on him prey;
> And these have smaller still to bite 'em;
> And so proceed ad infinitum.[21]

From the viewpoint of defending phagocytes, it is a cruel joke to place a new kidney or heart into the human body. It is alien tissue, therefore enemy, therefore to be attacked and destroyed. The first lesson learned in early attempts to graft borrowed tissue was that it was almost sure to be rejected. During the past ten years study has concentrated on ways to stop or bypass the defense that nature developed.

Several techniques have been tried. One is the injection of substances to impede the defenders. The second is a Trojan horse: Before surgery the recipient is inoculated with cells from the donor's body so that the defense will become acclimated to the invaders before the main volume of new tissue is emplaced. The third approach is tissue-matching: finding a donor organ whose cells are so similar to the recipient's that the defenders are fooled. In practice all three may play an important part.

The first efforts to block the immune system involved whole-body exposure to radiation. This stopped the graft rejection, but it was like burning a forest to destroy a tree. The radiation injured bone marrow and thereby the blood.

Several immunosuppressive drugs came into use, including cortisone, prednisone, and azothioprine, but the main breakthrough occurred in rediscovery of antilymphocytic serum (ALS). This was found in 1899 but not used as an immunosuppressant until 1967. ALS is formed by taking lymphocytes from the blood of the person who is donating an organ. This extract is injected into a horse, which produces antibodies against the white cells. Serum from the manufacturing animal is then injected into the person who is to receive the organ graft. The ALS damages the recipient's lymphocytes, slowing the reaction against the transplanted tissue.[22]

When Dr. Barnard came to his first heart transplant, he was armed with several tools to forestall rejection, which he knew would be the greatest danger, and he moved quickly to forestall it. Shortly after Washkansky's operation, immunosuppressive drugs had reduced his lymphocytes to 1 percent of normal. The defenders were not there to fight off the alien heart, nor were they present to fight off other disease. Infection crept in, gained a bridgehead in his lungs, and killed him in spite of massive doses of antibiotics.[23]

The grim irony is that 85 percent of the people who succumb under immunotherapy do so because of infection, not because of graft failure. Before transplant the body is already weak and easy prey to infection. If the remaining defense is destroyed, then any minor infection becomes sure death. Another complication is that such treatment may permit growth of some virus-induced cancers which otherwise would be controlled by the body itself.[24]

The main problem is overkill. Immunosuppressants can be truly effective only when we learn to defeat only that part of the defense which would attack the transplanted organ, leaving other armies free to fight other infection. Some progress is being made. By 1972 leading immunologists agreed generally that the defense consists of two armies: the infantry (antibodies sent out in response to invasion) and heavy armor (lymphocytes, which are largely responsible for rejecting grafts of foreign tissue). Learning how the two types of cells cooperate may lead to selective immunization.

Another hope involves a mysterious molecule known as the transfer factor. This can be obtained from the cells of healthy people and when transferred to a person suffering an immunity deficiency disease, gives him the immunological status of the donor. Inoculation with an organ donor's transfer factor might thus prevent the recipient from rejecting the organ.[25]

Replacing worn-out human parts will never be as simple as replacing an automobile engine because no part exactly fits any two people. Chances of success are greatest, however, when cells in new tissue are similar to those of the receiving host.

We seldom regard blood as an organ, yet this was the first tissue transferred from one person to another. Early transfusions were more likely to fail than succeed and for a time were forbidden by the church and some governments.

It was not until 1900 that Karl Landsteiner discovered there are four main blood groups. Infusion of the wrong group can cause rejection and death. It is routine practice now to match blood types between donor and recipient. Millions of pints of whole blood or plasma are collected and stored in hospitals, where massive quantities are sometimes needed. One operation in Chicago in 1970 involved planting an artificial heart valve in a man suffering from hemophilia, the bleeder's disease. Blood used during the operation was collected from 2,100 people and totaled 2,500 pints.[26]

Out of blood-typing and tissue-testing emerged new techniques to match tissue for transplanting organs. Although drugs may help induce a patient's system to accept a new organ, long-term survival depends greatly upon how close a tissue match was made. Kidney transplants offer evidence in point. During the early 1960's less than half of all kidney grafts functioned longer than a year. Best results occurred when the new kidney came from an identical twin. Survival in such cases was 88 percent. If the donor was a brother or other near relative, survival was about 50 percent; it was only 16 percent for unrelated recipients. Experience of later years improved the chances for life. By 1971, 80 percent of all kidneys donated by relatives remained functional after a year, and the survival rate from carefully matched cadaver kidneys had increased to 60 percent.[27]

The computer is proving a valuable tool in solving the complexities of differentiating human tissue. In Chicago pathologist George L. Wied uses a computerized microscope to analyze tissue samples. This super-consultant is designed for detecting cancer cells, but similar devices will help to reach closer tissue match for transplants as well.[28]

The School of Medicine at U.C.L.A. also uses the computer in tissue-typing. There, since 1963 Dr. Paul I. Terasaki and his staff have tissue-typed more than half of all the world's transplanted organs. He looks to the day when the body's reaction to a transplant may be predicted with such precision that the fear of rejection will be virtually nil. Terasaki works with ten hospitals in the Los Angeles area. Blood and tissue types of waiting patients are fed into the computer. Then, if a cadaver becomes available with a healthy organ to spare, the computer searches its list of waiting patients until a match is found. In one case a dead person's eyes, spleen, kidneys, liver, and large patches of skin were retrieved as donations.

Dr. Norman Shumway at Stanford University believes that by the end of the 1970's some two thousand to three thousand persons will receive new hearts each year, with 80 percent living a year or more after. He plans experiments in transplanting hearts and lungs together "because the axis is so closely related in function and so inter-dependent." He believes that liver transplants will also become common.[29]

Two other problems remain. One is the supply and preservation of spare parts. The other is defining the exact moment of death. Duplicate organs, such as a kidney, may be removed without serious harm to the donor, but there is only one heart. If it is removed more than thirty minutes after death, it is useless for transplant. Therefore the moments between one person's death and another's life are few. Surgeons are acutely aware that they live on a fragile borderline of questionable ethics and morality. As one physician wrote to *The New York Times*:

> The most disturbing aspect of the heart transplant procedure is the criterion of death. In order to transplant a heart it must be kept beating; otherwise it is biologically dead and of no use to the recipient. That means the heart must have the ability to restart its beat and then function normally. Is the donor of such a heart dead?[30]

The danger that a doctor might inadvertently hasten the death of a person to retrieve a vital organ has stimulated re-examination of traditional signals of death. This is important also because of the extraordinary methods now available to maintain semblances of life in a dying patient. The issue was placed in perspective by Dr. Harold Hillman, physiologist at the University of Surrey in England:

> If a person has been killed, an excised perfused kidney can go on producing urine, a transplanted heart can continue to beat, and even an udder can continue to give milk. Are these organs dead?
>
> We can think of death of the body, death of the organ, the tissue, the cell, or the enzyme. Nevertheless, it is clear that we mean something specific when we talk about death clinically —when we want to instruct the undertaker to proceed with burial. Death appears to be an increasing loss of organization

of the body, starting from the higher centers, progressing down through the tissues and cells to the enzymes.

This gives us the basis for a clinical definition of death. It is that state of the whole body in which the brain has *irreversibly* lost control of the spinal cord. This definition tells us when an organ may be taken out for transplantation. The difficulty is knowing when the change *is* irreversible.[31]

The most fertile place to wait for fresh human organs is the emergency ward of any big-city hospital. The best harvest time is a holiday weekend when the automobile yields up its quota of torn and broken bodies. Other human beings lie waiting, gasping for enough hours to find replacements for dying hearts, kidneys, lungs, spleens, or livers. The moment a bloody body becomes a cadaver, pathologists set to work cutting out salvageable parts. Tissue types are identified. Within minutes the fresh organs are delivered to the operating theater, where they are allotted and sewn into the fortunate people who will gain a few days, weeks, or months more of life.

The healer works against great odds. Thousands of lives could be saved, but there are not enough spare parts to go around. Even if there were, an organ can be kept viable for only a limited time. In most cases a patient dying in one city cannot produce an organ in time to save a person dying a thousand miles away. Finally, there is no clear definition of who owns a dead body. Doctors cannot remove organs without permission from the patient and his family.

Recognizing that there may never be a sufficient supply of spare human parts, some researchers have turned to animal sources. Pigs, sheep, calves, and apes may someday be tissue-conditioned so that their vital organs will be compatible with human recipients. Dr. Michael E. DeBakey at Houston has tried animal transplants with calf hearts and lungs from the slaughterhouse. Success in kidney transplants caused Dr. T. E. Starzl, of Denver, to extend his search for viable organs to the higher primates. A team from Johns Hopkins and Stellenbosch universities similarly worked with baboons in South Africa.[32]

Such a donor could conceivably be prepared specifically for a waiting patient and then slaughtered at the most propitious moment for the graft to take place.

In the meantime other scientists labor to extend the precious minutes an organ may be kept alive after removal. At U.C.L.A. Dr. Terasaki seeks to preserve tissue long enough for consignment and delivery on a nationwide basis. At any one time some six thousand Americans are awaiting new kidneys. If all these could be reached with new organs in time, by jet air shipment, the chance of finding ideal tissue matches would greatly improve.

So far, preservation of an animal organ for as much as three days still requires machinery too delicate for long-distance transportation. Dog hearts have been preserved up to seven hours in saline solution, up to thirty hours in a machine profusing it with nutrients, and up to four days when connected to a living host.[33] At Methodist Hospital in Houston Dr. John Liddicote and Dr. Edward B. Diethrich developed a portable chamber in which the heart and lungs, with no cut between, could be kept alive for twenty to thirty hours and transported to a distant location.[34]

The goal is a bank of live hearts beating in chambers waiting for transplant. Dr. Shumway at Stanford believes the day is near when a national system of organ banks will be in operation. "I think eventually we will have some kind of systemized tissue-typing," he said. "Citizens willing to be donors will carry this information on a bracelet or dog tag." If such a donor died anywhere in the nation, local doctors could remove and preserve appropriate organs with assurance that legal blocks, such as family permission, had already been cleared.

Ultimately the national (or international) system of human-organ banks could be keyed to a master computer programmed with a continuous up-to-date medical history of every person. This would include tissue-typing. If a person died, then he could be matched instantly with a patient in some other city waiting to receive an organ.

CHAPTER 5

The Body Shop

The first ancient priest who carved through skull to remove an evil spirit would be amazed to see the operating theater and the trappings that surround today's surgeon in the modern ritual of human repair.

Where a stone slab once awaited its victim in the temple, an operating table now stands in metallic purity beneath a battery of lights. Attendants are cloaked in sterilized garments, the germ-stink of their breath masked by gauze. Knives, scissors, chisels, suturing needles, catgut, silk, cotton, towels, all sterilized, are aligned in military precision. The surgeon's hands have been scrubbed and rescrubbed, then encased in sterile gloves. He holds these precious instruments of repair up before him to avoid the unconscious motion that might cause him to touch a contaminated surface.

The anesthetist stands ready with gas and hypodermic. Bottled blood hangs on its rack, a tube leading to the needle taped in the patient's arm vein. An ultraviolet machine irradiates the air to kill any bacteria which might have eluded the disinfectants. Electronic machines monitor pulse and heartbeat. A nurse charts breathing and changing body state.

This one is brain surgery. The patient lies tilted upward and receives a local anesthetic. Towels are stitched around the bottom of his skull. The pate is shaved and scoured.

The surgeon makes a deft cut around the patient's scalp and peels it back while an assistant mops up and ties off bleeding vessels. A rectangular patch of bone is scraped clean and burr holes drilled at the four corners. The trephine is motor-driven but is still an auger, cutting out buttons of bone. Mechanical safeguards and the surgeon's touch prevent drilling too deep, through membranes covering the brain.

Now a metal strip is fed into one button hole and inched out through another. Above this strip the surgeon cuts through skull with a wire saw. Three sides of the rectangle are cut; the fourth is left. The surgeon pries and lifts. Cracks form along the fourth side. The slab folds back, and a door is open to the human brain. Forceps clamp the cracked fourth side to squeeze off leaking blood. A three-layered membrane still protects the brain, but now this, too, is carefully opened.

From this point every nuance of the brain surgeon's skill must come to bear. If it is a tumor, he determines its size, perhaps snips a fragment for biopsy, and decides whether or not to remove it. He might lance an abscess. He might tie an abnormal swelling in a blood vessel.

For hours this team of surgeon, assistants, and nurses might work together with ballet precision before the work is done. Then blood vessels are tied. The operative field is flooded with salt solution and syphoned off and repeated to make sure no small blood vessel is left oozing. Membranes are stitched back in place. Bone is wired back. Scalp is sewed back. The patient's head is wrapped in a sterile white turban of gauze.

Now our primitive priest could return to his grave mystified by this modern magic, most of which he had not understood at all: razor-sharp instruments sparkling in a glare of sunless light; a patient who remained conscious but felt no pain; an invisible light to kill invisible spirits of infection. Truly the world had changed since his primeval moment on life's stage.

Completion of surgery is only the first phase of magic in the modern human-repair shop. From the operating theater the patient is wheeled into the recovery room. There after major surgery, be it brain, heart, or a malfunctioning gall bladder, the patient is watched moment by moment as his doped life processes gradually return. Bottled nutrient feeds through a needle into his bloodstream. Stomach contents may be pumped away through a tube inserted down a nostril. Nurses hover over him checking respiration and pulse. Other magic machines, now commonplace, measure electric pulses from heart or brain.

When the patient revives to a haze of pain and awareness, he is back in his hospital room, immobilized by a skein of tubing and wires hooked to machines that supplement his life forces until he can take up the task again. His urine has been checked for poison, blood analyzed for a dozen signs of health or infection, and film examined from an X-ray camera that peered within his body.

Anesthetic wears away. Pain localizes within the area violated by the knife, but before it becomes too severe, a brisk nurse appears with a hypodermic needle and administers an unceremonious jab to the buttocks. The cheerful surgeon hurries in to glance confidently at his handiwork, then out again to see another of the human mechanisms repaired on his assembly line.

Finally the patient lies staring at the ceiling in confused misery. He is dimly aware, however, that in the sterile room of the marvelous body shop he had delivered his life, for a little while, into the hands of competent doctors and technicians armed with chemicals and tools to lengthen his healthy years. In the night his fitful sleep may be interrupted by the cool fingers of a nurse checking his pulse. He is watched. Someone cares.

It was not always so. Through much of the past two thousand years hospitals were dreaded as much as the dungeon. Dark, cheerless halls, reeking with the stench of urine, feces, and infection, were the hallmarks of the hostel of last resort. The hospital was the place where the poor went to die.

The idea of a central place for treating the sick probably originated in the Babylonian custom of bringing infirm patients into the marketplace for medical consultation. Ancient Greeks and other cultures maintained common rooms for the sick in association with pagan temples.[1] The Romans maintained a chain of military hospitals to support the Empire. Two of these, excavated near Bonn and on the Danube, date to the first century A.D. and were the best of their kind known in antiquity.[2]

The dedicated spirit of ministering to human suffering on a large scale, however, was born with Christianity. One early hospital was founded by Fabiola about the year 400 "to gather in the sick from the streets and to nurse the wretched sufferers, wasted with poverty and disease."[3] Based on the obligation of charity and hospitality, many hospitals were founded by religious orders. Clinics were maintained by monks beside Christian cloisters. The Hôtel Dieu at Lyons, France, was founded in A.D. 542.[4]

While the sciences decayed or remained static in Europe, care of the sick out of pure compassion rose to hitherto unknown heights. Borrowing from Christians, India, and their own convictions, the Arabs developed excellent hospitals. These joined the medical arts that the Muhammadan world kept alive while Europe sank into social decay. As early as A.D. 707 Caliph El Welid founded a hospital at Damascus. Dispensaries and infirmaries sprang up in all important cities. In 1160 the largest and best-appointed Muhammadan hospital was built at Damascus, where the ill were treated and drugs dispensed free of charge for three centuries.[5]

In 1487 Queen Isabella of Spain introduced the field hospital (*ambulancia*) during the siege of Málaga. In the German army the sick and wounded were sent to the baggage train, congregated in a tent, treated by a surgeon, and cared for by women of the twilight—the camp followers. It requires little imagination to visualize the horror of such a hospital in any war.

Except for Roman Catholic orders, in which discipline and decency prevailed, the image of filth and corruption dominated the public view of hospitals. As late as 1857 the servant nurses in London were referred to in the *Times* as women "lectured by committees, preached at by chaplains, scowled on by treasurers and stewards, scolded by matrons, sworn at by surgeons, bullied by [wound] dressers, grumbled at and abused by patients, insulted if old and ill-favored, talked flippantly to if middle-aged and good humoured, tempted and seduced if young and well-looking."[6]

All this was changed by an angry young woman named Florence Nightingale, a name that still carries the ring of compassion and cheer, coupled with tough determination, which marks the passage of great women through the untidy, brutish, and often absurd world of men. Born in 1820 in Florence, Miss Nightingale was destined for a brilliant marriage and a life among the aristocracy, but from her earliest years she felt compelled to attend the sick. It was only by overcoming violent family objections that she was able to obtain training as a nurse in Germany. She was thirty-three when she received her first major task, that of reorganizing the Institution for the Care of Sick Gentlewomen in Distressed Circumstances, a small London hospital.

That job well done plunged her into the mainstream. In 1854 England and France were at war with Russia in the Crimea. Britain seethed with indignation over reports that the faraway military hospitals were in poor condition. Sidney Herbert, Secretary of War, asked Miss Nightingale to help. Within weeks she sailed for the Crimea with a task force of thirty-eight hastily recruited nurses.

These courageous women, dressed in drab gray uniforms, stepped ashore in the mud of Scutari across from Constantinople in time to greet five hundred wounded men, remnants of the famous charge of the Light Brigade in the Battle of Balaclava. Two thirds of the British cavalrymen were killed or wounded there in twenty-five minutes.

A lesser woman would have taken the ship back to England. The hospitals were vast dilapidated buildings, old Turkish barracks, filthy, bare, and destitute of every convenience. Medical supplies, food, and bedding had not arrived.

Miss Nightingale did not know the bacterial theory of infection, but she knew that cleanliness, fresh air, pure water, light, and drainage were the surest means of preventing it. She found a few men well enough to clean up the mess and put them to work. She organized her thirty-eight nurses into a schedule of care, diet preparation, and kitchen work. In those first terrible days Florence Nightingale worked slavishly through the day. At night the "lady of the lamp" walked the miles of corridors, leaving a word of comfort at each pallet. Within a month she had five thousand men under her care—men who came to worship her as the one sign of compassion and tenderness from home.

Her biggest problem was cutting through a vast web of apathy, bureaucratic sloth, and jealousy. Somehow she kept a stream of correspondence flowing to England, demanding doctors, nurses, and supplies. She caught a fever that nearly killed her but refused to return to England, declaring: "I can stand out the war with any man."

She did. Countless lives were saved, and her work set the stage for hospital reform around the world. She returned to England a heroine. When she died in 1910, Miss Nightingale's body was carried to rest in a small English churchyard by six sergeants of the British army.[7]

Thus tonight, in the flickering shadows cast through the years by Florence Nightingale's lamp, a nurse in white uniform will forget her aching feet long enough to take a patient's temperature, check his pulse with cool fingers, and inject a soothing drug to ease his pain.

Tender care and the physician's educated instincts will remain the prime tools of healing, but through the years instruments to extend these faculties have accumulated like building stones in the edifice of human existence. Each has contributed to the rebuilding of men to longer, healthier lives.

First came the surgeon's wares and a family of tools to peer into the orifices of the body. In 1600 the Paduan professor Santorio Santorio (called Sanctorious) invented a clinical thermometer and pulse clock, but these were forgotten for a hundred years.[8] The stethoscope, that ubiquitous instrument which one imagines a doctor wears even to bed, was invented in 1819 by the French physician René Théophile Hyacinthe Laennec. The first one was a simple tube of paper. With this and improved models, Dr. Laennec studied the diagnostic sounds of heart and lung diseases and wrote aural descriptions of bronchitis, peritonitis, pneumonia, and pulmonary tuberculosis.[9]

The recognition of germs, use of antiseptics to kill some of them, and the emerging science of anesthesia established hospitals as a place where healing and surgery could reach greater numbers with promise of life. The physician stretched his senses to gain deeper understanding of patient problems. Efforts to explain life—and the universe—in mechanistic formulas led to an outpouring of mechanical, chemical, and electrical devices to test the organs and fluids of the body and extend the physician's diagnostic powers. Many of these, including laboratory blood tests, were so complex or expensive that the hospital, available to many doctors at once, became the only central work center for testing as well as healing.

One of the greatest medical tools resulted from the discovery of X rays in 1895 by Wilhelm C. Roentgen. Although dangerous if misused, the X-ray camera opened a window to the inside of the body. It reveals broken bones, the location of a foreign body such as a bullet, and, under special application, the presence of an abscess, gallstones, and other pathological conditions such as cancer.[10] Experts warn against the careless and indiscriminate use of X rays for diagnostic purposes because of danger to reproductive cells and other cell destruction leading to cancer.

X-ray technology also has grown more sophisticated. Dr. F. Mason Sones, Jr., a Cleveland cardiologist, developed X-ray movies to aid diagnosis of heart and artery disease. The process is known as cine coronary angiography. A thin tube is inserted into an artery of the arm and guided carefully up through the aorta. Then a dye, opaque to X rays, is squirted into the coronary arteries. This shows up on a motion-picture X ray, revealing with 90 percent accuracy where an artery may be blocked.[11]

Ranking in importance with X ray are the electrocardiograph, developed by Willem Einthoven in 1903, and the electroencephalograph, first demonstrated in 1929 by Hans Berger, of Germany. The electrocardiograph measures pulses of electricity from the heart. These are translated into ink tracings on graph paper (electrocardiogram or EKG), from which an analyst can detect a number of abnormal heart conditions, often in time to forestall critical illness or death. The electroencephalograph similarly measures and records the electrical impulses generated by nerve cells in the brain. The resulting electroencephalogram (EEG) enables doctors to diagnose epilepsy, locate brain tumors, or determine if the brain has been injured.

Many advances in medical technology have been the by-products of war. Thus it was that radioisotopes, a keystone of modern diagnosis, became commonly available because of the atomic bombs that fell on Japan in World War II. Isotopes are forms of basic elements which emit radiation. They are created in considerable quantities in the fission of uranium. Microscopic amounts of certain isotopes, circulating in the organs of the body, can be detected and their motion interpreted as symptoms of health or disease. Radioisotopes are also more efficient agents than X rays or radium in cancer therapy.

Radioactive iodine was one of the first isotopes used in diagnosis because of its affinity with the thyroid gland. The neutral form of the element is used normally in the thyroid and tends to concentrate there. When the radioactive form became available, doctors could administer it in small quantities and monitor its concentration and passage through the gland by using a radiation counter. This has aided greatly in diagnosing and treating thyroid problems.

Radioactive strontium, related to calcium, settles in the bones. These and other isotopes, such as cobalt, present a two-edged sword. They are valuable tools to diagnose and treat illness, but also they are dangerous sources of radiation which may cause long-term tissue damage and cancer if not contained and controlled.

Many isotopes decay so quickly that it has been difficult to use them as medical tools. To eliminate delays in shipment from a remote source, the Medical Center at U.C.L.A. installed a $340,000 cyclotron to manufacture short-lived elements on the premises. These may be put to work immediately. One is carbon 11. According to Dr. Norman MacDonald, professor of radiology, this offers promise in diagnosing coronary heart disease, for locating tumors, and for learning more about brain metabolism.[12]

Scientists at Oak Ridge Associated Universities in Tennessee reported that another short-lived isotope may become important for locating and measuring tumors. It is gallium 67, a relative of aluminum, with a half-life of three and one-fourth days. Two or three days after receiving an injection of the isotope, a patient is placed under a scanning machine. The tumor, where radioactivity has concentrated, will show up on the viewing screen. According to Dr. Gould Andrews, the technique reveals size and location of tumors deep within body tissue without the destruction caused by exploratory surgery and can show if a cancer is spreading or receding as the result of radiation or chemical therapy.[13]

One of the longest searches in medical technology culminated in 1953 when the American surgeon John H. Gibbon first used a machine capable of purifying and pumping blood through a patient's system bypassing the heart. This is the now well-known heart-lung machine, which made the first heart transplants possible. Use of these intricate and expensive machines has enabled heart surgeons to save thousands of lives by lengthening the amount of time available to work with the open heart. Circulation of blood outside the body has been limited, however, because techniques that transfer oxygen and carbon dioxide also damage the blood itself.[14]

The National Heart Institute recently reported a new gas transfer method which reduces this damage to the blood and extends the hours available for complex heart surgery. Some other heart-lung machines have utilized a membrane to accomplish the transfer of oxygen from the carrier liquid to the patient's blood being circulated through the machine and the simultaneous extraction of carbon dioxide. Resistance in the membrane has been one of the factors causing damage to the blood.

The new concept in blood oxygenation developed by Abcor, Inc., of Cambridge, Massachusetts, and the Cleveland Clinic brings the machine's carrier fluid and the patient's blood in direct contact with each other, by circulating them in opposite directions through a Teflon tube or between parallel plates. The experimenters reported that this technique provides a higher rate of gas transfer to and from the blood and thus less contact with artificial surfaces which cause blood damage.[15]

To those who don't know her well, Helen Turner (the name is not her real one) is a normal, healthy high-school junior who lives in a midwestern city. A blonde with gray-blue eyes, Helen is a cheerful, fun-loving class-leader, an above-average student, and a cheerleader at football and basketball games. Her plans for the future include college, then maybe a husband and a family of her own.

But Helen is far from normal. From time to time she looks pale and lacks her usual energy. An elastic bandage on her left arm conceals a loop of plastic tubing through which blood is constantly flowing from an artery into a vein. Helen never travels to out-of-town games and is constantly on guard against infections, even a simple head cold.

Three times a week this young woman checks in at a major

hospital. She always has the same bed and knows the nurses and house doctors almost as well as her own family. For about eight hours each visit the tubes in her forearm are connected to a remarkable machine through which her blood must be circulated and recirculated. For more than three years, since her kidneys failed, this medical routine has been an unvarying part of Helen's life. It may continue for as long as she lives.[16]

The machine is the so-called artificial kidney, an ingenious mechanism of pumps and membranes which can take over the job of cleansing blood when human kidneys have failed. Invented in the 1940's, the kidney machine has saved the lives of many people, but remaining alive by this process may cost ten thousand to fifteen thousand dollars a year. Only a few hundred people in the nation now enjoy availability of a machine, or monetary resources, for this treatment. In 1971 scientists at the Atomic Energy Commission's Argonne National Laboratory near Chicago reported development of a miniature artificial kidney which can do the job as well at a fraction of the cost. The throwaway blood filter, made of cellophane in a package smaller than a book, can be used at home at a cost of about three thousand dollars a year.

Technical imitations of the intricate functions of the human mechanism even include an artificial womb, developed paradoxically as a by-product of the spreading practice of abortion. Dr. Lawrence Lawn, of Cambridge University, said he had kept fetuses alive for several hours using a mechanical device similar to the heart-lung machine to supply the tiny bodies with oxygen and nutrients. Dr. Lawn believes the machine will prove valuable in saving babies born too early to survive.[17]

Out of the nation's space program has emerged a family of new devices to assist the healing arts. One is a television transmitter so small that it can be swallowed in a capsule and send out pictures of the workings of the stomach. Small hearing aids are made from transistors. A heart-pulse device developed for astronauts can regulate the heartbeat of cardiac patients. Ball bearings the size of pinpoints are used to make ultra-high-speed dental drills. An electronic method to improve the clarity of photos transmitted from Mars has provided startling results in sharpening the vague outlines of X-ray pictures. Technologists are now considering radio transmitters—small as grains of dust—which can float in the bloodstream and transmit information about health and disease.

Part of the new technology has been named bionics, the marriage of electronics to biology.

"One of the things we're learning from it is how to duplicate bodily functions," said Eugene E. Horton, chief of NASA's Manned Flight Awareness Office in Houston. "Through implanted instrumentation, the heartbeat signals of an animal have been transmitted thirty feet, using only the electric energy generated within the animal's body.

"This is only the honeymoon. What bionics could be doing for you in twenty years excites the imagination. Your doctor may one day be constantly tuned in to your heart by such a transmitter that gives a readout in his office. If your heart starts to act up, he'll receive a little blip on his recorder and advise you to come in for a checkup."[18]

Closed-circuit television has become a routine teaching aid to show medical students a surgeon's-eye view of operations and allow nurses to watch patients without being at the bedside. Television can also help a doctor see and diagnose a patient at a distance. One such Tele-Diagnosis system links Boston's Logan International Airport with Massachusetts General Hospital. It was developed to help people who fall ill while traveling.

In one case a fifty-five-year-old businessman suffered pain while flying and feared he was having a heart attack. The pilot radioed ahead and alerted a nurse, who met the man as he disembarked. In a room equipped with closed-circuit television and two-way radio she took the man's history and phoned his symptoms to a doctor at the hospital. The doctor then questioned the patient by radio while examining him visually by color television. In this case the man was assured he was suffering flight discomfort and indigestion and was sent on his way. If the ailment had been more serious, the radio-television system would have saved precious minutes in getting him to a hospital.[19]

A similar time and cost saving now permits long-distance telephone examinations of heart patients recuperating at home. A nurse visits the patient with a portable EKG machine. Once it is hooked up, she plugs it into the telephone, after calling the patient's doctor, and the electrocardiogram is transmitted to a receiving machine in the doctor's office. There he can read the EKG and give appropriate advice in a matter of moments.

In 1970 at Battelle Northwest, the Richland, Washington, laboratories of Battelle Memorial Institute, doctors were treated to a unique television show. What they saw was a real time "movie" of an unborn child in a mother's womb. Gray images on the screen moved as the child moved, and by special focusing it was possible to see inside the body of the fetus with an almost three-dimensional effect. When the mother shifted to a new position, the picture clearly revealed that the child was a boy.

The unique part of the demonstration was that the pictures they watched came not from light or X ray, but from ultrasound—sound waves above the range of the human ear. The process, known as acoustic holography, was developed to permit imaging the inside of the body without using X rays, which may cause tissue damage and cell mutations. Radiation danger is especially great for the unborn child, and thus doctors have traditionally been denied the tool of X-ray examination in diagnosing progress of pregnancy and detecting prenatal abnormalities.

In acoustic holography ultrasound waves of various frequencies are transmitted through the body. Different tissues provide various return signals according to the frequency and thus permit careful focusing. The signals are then changed to visual images and projected on the television screen. Research scientists at Battelle have viewed structural details of a rat embryo less than one-half inch long, tumor growth on the liver and stomach wall of a mouse, the inside of rabbit kidney and intestine, and well-defined images of a human fetus at less than three months' gestation.

"Using this device, it is possible to look at any single focal plane as you search with sound through the body cavity," said John Deichman, associate manager of applied physics. "Picture resolution is determined by the frequency of sound which illuminates the object, even though the object may be small and surrounded by layers of body tissue. Acoustic holography allows picture resolution of soft tissue as well as bone, something X rays cannot easily do."

"The ability to image the uterus without exposure to X ray will be of tremendous value to the medical world," said John Rasmussen, program coordinator. "There are definite advantages in being able to observe continuously an image of uterine movements and contractions as they occur."

Melvin R. Silov, pathologist, added: "I can see many potential uses, including early sex determination of the fetus and detection of abnormalities during gestation. Other possible uses would be in determining the exact location of blood clots for surgical removal and interior imaging of organs while surgery is in progress." The Battelle program is sponsored by the U.S. Agency for International Development.[20]

At Vanderbilt University in Nashville, Tennessee, experimenters are using sound waves to measure how well a broken bone may be healing. According to Dr. Paul H. King, sound waves sent through the bone are measured on an oscilloscope and analyzed by a computer. By comparing the results with a measurement from a person's unbroken limb doctors can tell whether the patient's broken bone has healed.[21]

During the past decade new tools to aid diagnosis, treatment, and surgery have poured from technical laboratories almost faster than they can be utilized. The prime goal is that of providing more precise information while reducing the labor burden on doctors, nurses, and technicians. Efforts are focused on detecting incipient organ failure or disease before it happens rather than treating the unforeseen emergency.

Knitting all of the new body-shop techniques together is the computer, which can coordinate testing, observation, and analysis and condense thousands of hours of investigative work to minutes. Although the computer can never replace final judgment of the physician, it can extend his capabilities to make maximum use of limited time.

Routine physical examination is a case in point. Since 1965 more than fifty multiphasic screening centers, where some 250,000 people a year now receive electronic examinations, have been set up in the United States. The patient moves from machine to machine, which asks yes or no questions about his health. A nurse takes a blood sample which the computer analyzes. Twenty-four tests of the blood can be done in less than an hour. At the end the computer prints out a reading for the doctor, who can determine in a few minutes if a problem exists. Physicians regard such screening, which can be done for less than one hundred dollars a patient and save up to five hundred dollars in laboratory fees, as an ideal way to examine large numbers of people and provide early warning of disease. Computers are also programmed with case histories, which can be retrieved at the touch of a typewriter key, saving time normally consumed by a file clerk fumbling for a folder.

At one computerized center in Chicago Dr. Marvin Klein screened hundreds of members of a labor union. He found signs of the eye disease glaucoma in six. Two would have gone blind without prompt treatment. Dr. Klein estimates that the cost of supporting these two men for life, if their blindness had developed, would have been greater than the cost of the computer's operation for five years.

Technicians at the Mary Hitchcock Memorial Hospital in Hanover, New Hampshire, have programmed a computer to sort through twenty thousand different radiation treatment plans and extract the ten most suitable for a particular cancer patient. In five minutes the machine replaces several hours of painstaking work by a trained technician.[22]

Medical researchers at Stanford University are using the computer to match drugs with dangerous microorganisms to help physicians prescribe the exact drug to combat specific infection. This process gains in importance as viruses and bacteria mutate to build resistance to compounds that once killed them. The computer's quality control improves test reliability, gives improved diagnosis, and allows timelier treatment with less medical paper work. Information on more than nineteen thousand organisms, isolated from patients at the Stanford hospital, has been stored in the computer, which will continue "learning" as it receives new and changing information. A check on a specific case requires less than ten seconds and costs five cents. Other hospitals are able to tap into the information by direct telephone line.[23]

Electronic devices controlled by computer can now monitor the condition of critically ill patients and provide doctors with split-second bedside reports. When a patient enters the Center for the Critically Ill, operated by University of Southern California physicians at Hollywood Presbyterian Hospital, he is linked by tubes and wires to electronic sensors which monitor up to twenty-six physiological conditions at once and display the information on a screen above the patient's bed. According to Dr. Max H. Weil, the computer provides a "prognostic index" which tells a doctor at any given moment a patient's chances of survival.

Some of the functions tested are heart rate, blood pressure, and temperature. More exotic measurements include analysis of the blood-chemical lactate, the level of which is an indication of health or severity of illness.

One of the prognostic findings revealed by the mechanized doctor is that the temperature of the big toe is an exceedingly accurate indicator of how well the patient is doing. According to Dr. Weil, if the temperature of the big toe remains midway between the patient's body temperature and the room temperature, it's a good sign. If the toe temperature drops below that point within three hours after the patient is admitted, his outlook for life is poor.

The equipment at the center was designed to monitor patients in shock. Now it is trained to watch many kinds of illness. Eventually doctors hope to program it to deliver drugs directly into the patient's bloodstream as needed.

One of the physician's most difficult tasks is forming an overall impression of a patient's condition using the results of many tests made in conventional ways. The doctor is unable to manipulate in his head more than three or four rapidly changing factors at once. The new equipment does this automatically.

"The things we are doing look mechanical, cold, and dehumanizing, but really they are not," Dr. Weil said. "It frees doctors and nurses from mechanical tasks and gives them the opportunity to devote themselves to the humanizing and professionally more-challenging aspects. Ultimately we are thinking of creating mechanical facilities that will improve care and at the same time reduce the need for highly trained technicians. We would let technology fill the void, and yet not ignore the human and medical needs of these patients."[24]

Beyond computerized hospitals the time is approaching when medical records of everyone could be programmed into a central computer for instantaneous readout anywhere, anytime. In this transient nation many families move several times in a generation and at the same time change family doctors. Each time, a part of a person's medical history stays behind and is lost. A central computer bank could keep a lifelong record of every individual so that any doctor anywhere could tap this information by telephone and be able to diagnose and prescribe more wisely.

Dr. Prosper Eckert, coinventor of the computer, said in 1971 that memory devices now available can retrieve and write a page of information in the blink of an eye from a file of information ten times greater than the *Encyclopaedia Britannica*. He estimated that for about $300,000,000 dossiers could be assembled on every person in the world. This instantly available information could be maintained and periodically updated for a few pennies per person.[25] The prospect of such an ultimate development in computerized information may be discomforting to many people. Although ideal for medical purposes, such a knowledge bank would be dangerous with unscrupulous persons or a monolithic government that could use the information for citizen surveillance and control. For the time being most people would prefer that their medical records be held in private by their doctor or hospital.

Chicago's $1,500,000 Cancer Prevention Center has an automated screening program covering a spectrum of diseases. "Our interest is in the theoretically healthy population," said Dr. Frank Paloucek. "If we can find symptoms of disease in the early state, an individual can be saved pain and the great cost of dealing with a full-blown disease later." He pointed out that practicing physicians are fully occupied caring for the sick. "In 1900," he said, "there were ninety million Americans and the medical schools graduated five thousand physicians a year. Now we have a population of two hundred million and graduate only seven thousand doctors a year."[26]

His point is well taken. The body shop of human repair has become a place of magical devices. A man, woman, or child may be nestled within a computerized womb of machines, electronics, and chemicals capable of continuing the life processes even after vital organs have stopped—a condition once known as death. Yet only a select few may take advantage of the wonders medical science has to offer. There are not enough doctors to go around, and the machines devised to ease their work have contributed to the mushrooming cost of medical care.

There are about seven thousand hospitals in the United States. We have some 330,000 doctors. Health maintenance costs nearly $70,000,000,000 a year, an average of more than $300 for every person. In spite of this, America ranks only twelfth internationally in infant mortality. Men in seventeen other countries live longer, and women in ten. Because of the high cost and scarcity of facilities in many areas, 40,000,000 Americans rarely see a physician. While technology shells out miracles, few ways are found to train more medical personnel, organize hospitals for more efficient service, and knit together private and public facilities.

As an example of medical costs, a friend of the author's suffered a severe heart attack and was taken to a private hospital. Despite intensive care, he died ten days later. The bill, left for his widow to pay, was $11,000. A heart-lung machine may cost $17,000 to buy and $50,000 a year to maintain. Heart-transplant surgery may cost $25,000 or more.[27] Cost of health insurance has become prohibitive, but without it the average family faces poverty and destitution if a serious illness should strike.

These mounting problems prompted Rand Corporation specialists to question how many medical breakthroughs the American public can afford. Dr. Thomas L. Lincoln and Dr. Palmer T. Van Dyke pointed out that the question has existed at least since the Greek Heraclitus in the fifth century, who complained: "Doctors cut, burn and torture the sick, and then demand of them an undeserved fee for such services." Now the questions are infinitely more complicated.

"In contrast to other industrial nations," the two men said, "it is here in the United States that the health-care system penalizes the poor and the ignorant, here that skyrocketing costs threaten to place adequate medical treatment beyond the means of even the moderately affluent, here that a growing bureaucracy depersonalizes the delivery of health services, and here that fragmentation and conflict among medical specialties threaten to force each patient to diagnose and manage his own ills. . . . The ever-increasing investment of manpower and resources in medical services has not even brought us nearer to a biological utopia devoid of disease."[28]

In partial response to the wave of almost desperate criticism, Elliot L. Richardson, Secretary of Health, Education, and Welfare, in 1971 set as his goal the better distribution of health care:

> We need to shift our perspective only very little to bring into focus problems of maldistribution and inefficient use of resources. Richly provided as we are with the manpower and facilities with which to deliver high quality health care, we find that these resources are concentrated in major metropolitan areas and seriously lacking in rural America and in both urban and rural poverty areas.
>
> Moreover, our utilization of these resources is often inefficient, wasteful, and unnecessarily costly. Patterns of health care delivery tend to encourage the excessive use of the most costly forms of care, notably hospitalization. This in turn has led to severe overcrowding of municipal hospitals and to duplicative proliferation of highly expensive equipment and facilities.[29]

Nearly two years after this pronunciamento, there were few signs of change for the better. Our new age thus differs little, except in magnitude, from the old, when good medical care was the exclusive right of nobles and kings. The wealthy and powerful profit first, but now there is some promise that the new medical marvels may someday bring better health and longer lives to everyone. In the meantime at least those who can pay the price may now enter the wonderful body shop for repairs, including installation of new parts when old ones wear out.

CHAPTER 6

Artificial
Men

The science and engineering of prosthetics—artificial parts for humans—probably began with the first caveman who mustered courage and stamina to prop a tree branch under his arm and hobble home after his leg was torn off by a tiger. That was a crutch.

Next to come were probably the peg leg, strapped to a stump of thigh, and the iron hook to augment a lost arm—both symbols of the gory folklore descended to us in savage but glamorous tales of piracy and buried treasure.

The peg leg, the crutch, the hook, and the cosmetic glass eye—all these served through many ages to shore up the bodies and ego of mutilated men, enabling them to continue active if not completely whole lives.

Today we still reap the legacy of human savagery and prop up our war-torn men with arms that work and legs that walk. Aluminum, plastic, and electronics are more sophisticated than the wooden crutch and peg leg. We have become so clever in devising artificial parts that seldom do we see an adult limp to remind us of the children crippled during the dread years of polio.

Today we delve inside to replace diseased parts with plastic and drive human hearts with electric power packs. We have artificial bones and artificial blood. We are precocious children, struggling valiantly to simulate God's work.

Tomorrow we may succeed. By trial and error we will find better ways to repair broken men. We also may succeed in the artificial extension of men's powers beyond the road map of evolution, or we may artificially hasten the evolution of men to a form bearing little resemblance to man at all. These long-range consequences of our mechanical quest were questioned by an editorial writer for *The Wall Street Journal*:

> What happens to society in general when many people can, with these aids, live much longer than today's already lengthened lives? The peril of population growth presses now; will the widespread use of artificial organs not intensify it? What happens to the people themselves? Will the artificiality eventually amount, in effect, to mutation? Will they, or will they *be able* to, maintain the standards and behavior that civilization regards as enduringly human?[1]

This comment aimed principally at the emotional turmoil aroused by early heart transplants, but it also focused on the older question: Are we playing God with artificial gadgetry?

Gernot Friese, medical director of the Ludwigsburg District Hospital in Germany, answered:

> The layman who has no experience with the treatment of sick human beings may ask this question justifiably. To the doctor the question is not the problem which it may appear to be.
>
> After all, every doctor learns during his work that the best, most "reliable" methods of treatment do not always succeed. Why do they work in one case and not in another? The doctor with many years of experience does not know—but he may gain the impression that his help is effective only when he acts in accordance with the plan of creation, or to put it in a different way, if he becomes an instrument of God.[2]

Therefore, social complications of the next century must rank behind immediate compassion when we rig a harness to give mobility to thalidomide babies born with stumps for arms and legs. Technicians must be instruments of God when they use metal pins and plastic to bolt together shattered bones of a Vietnam veteran so that he may walk out of the hospital and take up his work again.

In a practical sense the human race might well advance faster along the blind road of evolution if we permitted our diseased and defective to die quickly and remove themselves from the genetic pool. If those people unable to care for themselves were methodically eliminated, new generations would undoubtedly be stronger and healthier. Yet we would lose the essence of humanity itself if—under the uncomfortable pressures exerted by our multiplying billions—we were to lose the drive to heal and mend the defective.

In the half century since World War I wide progress has been made in materials and mechanisms to provide mobility and shape to the maimed, crippled, paralyzed, and deformed. These range from sophisticated and realistic artificial limbs to plastic materials which may be injected to return contour and beauty to a sagging face or flabby breast.

The prosthetic leg has graduated from a stump of wood. Now made of aluminum, steel, and plastic, synthetic legs are jointed at the knee and ankle to move as a real leg. The foot is shaped to fit a shoe. The amputee's power to walk may be enhanced by cords, pulleys, levers, and powered mechanisms which provide crude similarity to muscles and tendons. But in the case of paralysis or amputation, nervous control from the brain is gone, and the problem is to find ways to restore realistic semblance of this control. This is most vital in hand and arm, prime tools of manipulation, and it is here that greatest progress has occurred.

Early mechanical arms provided an elbow joint and metal pincers to replace the hand. By 1967 technicians had developed power-driven false arms using compressed gas, or electric motors with hydraulic actuators. Researchers sought linkages that would permit a person to think in terms of what he wanted to do rather than in terms of moving individual mechanical joints.

In Calgary, Canada, a twenty-four-year-old man whose leg was amputated after a motorcycle accident required only three hours to learn to walk on an artificial leg with an electric knee developed by a team of researchers at the Calgary General Hospital. George Clynch, who heads the technical team, said the device automatically locks to prevent buckling—a problem with most artificial legs. The leg uses a geared-down electric motor, small enough to fit inside the artificial limb along with batteries that operate for three days without recharging.[3]

The primary goal is to use electric impulses from muscles and nerves in the remaining portion of an arm or leg to trigger electric motors in the artificial limbs. Russian technicians were pioneers in this field. As early as 1964 the Soviet Union reported the invention of a bioelectrically operated artificial hand able to perform delicate movements. Additional work was done by the Rehabilitation Institute of Montreal on the myoelectric system, which uses action of existing muscles to provide the intermediate step. This laid the base for planting tiny electric receivers to pick up nerve and muscle signals and transmit them to powered machinery in the arm and hand. By 1972 a number of technical teams were experimenting with carbon as a prosthetic material, because it is not rejected by the body's internal system and may also be able to conduct electric impulses directly from nerve endings in an arm or leg stump to the artificial limb.

An Austrian company has begun volume production of artificial hands, and Swedish scientists have devised one with independently moving fingers.[4] A battery-powered arm activated by electric signals from muscles was tested in Boston in 1968.[5]

Finding the proper place to install miniaturized electronic receiver-transmitters has been a problem. The Russians used external electrodes. In Canada experimenters planted the transmitter in the marrow cavity of the bone. A Scandinavian team used a small plastic-covered capsule planted within the muscle tissue of the stump. Electronic signals from this device could be detected several yards away.[6] In Yugoslavia technicians installed small pressure sensors in the fingertips and palm of a mechanical hand to assist the user to vary his grip. Another approach, by V. L. Nickel in California, helps patients with severe paralysis of the upper limbs. Equipped with prosthetic attachments, the patient can move his hands and arms by controlling switches with his *tongue*.[7]

Now it is possible to contemplate the day when a person who had lost all four limbs could be fitted with new ones operating electrically with signals transmitted from the brain and spinal cord by remaining nerves and muscle. With external power such artificial limbs could be more efficient and stronger than natural arms and legs, though that level of technical excellence lies in the future.

In 1970 a twenty-one-year-old man was badly crushed in a train accident in East London, South Africa. His body was so severely damaged below the waist that doctors performed the most drastic amputation, hemicorporectomy, which means literally sawing a person in half. Despite the loss of all his body from the pelvis down, the young man recovered. Within nine months his terrible wounds had healed. His remaining torso was fitted with a fiberglass harness to which were attached two artificial legs. After extensive physical therapy he was able to stand upright and propel himself between parallel bars and get about in a wheelchair without help.[8] Before this landmark case this extreme resort to save life was limited to rare cases of cancer of the pelvis. After the lower part of the body was removed, the upper torso was kept alive by providing openings for the large bowel and urinary passage.

Such extreme measures are rare, but they show how far science may go to keep a human being alive and capable of useful function. For lesser handicaps electronic miniaturization has produced improved hearing aids which allow the virtually deaf to hear. Eyes may be saved by flexible contact lenses and implanted plastic corneas. Some ninety thousand people in the United States are blind because of scars on the eye lens. Perhaps a fourth of these can benefit from corneal transplants. Others may receive new plastic lenses made of materials that can be screwed into the eyeball to fit optical prescriptions.[9]

A Soviet surgeon in 1971 restored the sight of a man whose eyes were burned by chemicals by fabricating a new right eye from the rear half of his left eye. An artificial lens was inserted into the tissue before it was grafted onto the right eye. There was no pupil in the new eye, however, and two months after the first operation Dr. Mikhail Krasnov cut a small hole in the grafted tissue to make a pupil. "It took only two minutes to cut a small hole in the grafted tissue, and the world of color and light returned to the man," the surgeon said.[10]

Other experimental devices to assist the blind include a portable television camera which, when coupled with an acoustic perception system, helps a person locate obstacles in his path. Another approach is that of reaching directly into the sight centers of the brain. In one test a radio receiver was connected to electrodes planted in a fifty-two-year-old blind man's brain. Radio signals caused him to experience sensations of light in half of his visual field. Someday an artificial device in the brain may permit the blind to avoid obstacles or even read print and handwriting.[11]

Fitting people with spare parts and accessories is more than an exercise in preserving life. For thousands, such repairs mean the difference between living a vegetative existence or performing useful work. In 1969, for example, 242,000 handicapped persons benefited from governmental programs in vocational rehabilitation. For every one dollar invested in rebuilding people to useful lives, the government will reap five dollars in income taxes.

Fitting man-made parts to the outside of the body is one thing. Installing them inside is another. This requires materials that will do their job without damaging tissue or triggering the body's rejection mechanism.

One of the more merciful forms of surgery is replacement of joints painfully welded into immobility by arthritis. The first ball-and-socket artificial joint was fashioned in 1951, and by 1966 surgeons were successful with metal joints cemented into the femur, or thighbone, of elderly patients.[12]

This operation is not uncommon now, but materials are still experimental. Most plastics are not hard enough to bear the load of the legs. Metals are still best, though an artificial hip-bone and joint are heavy and must be cast rather than machined. More promising is research in powder metallurgy. Work at the University of Wisconsin has produced porous metallic materials with properties closely resembling bone.[13] Experiments with carbon fibers, which are light but stronger than steel, also show promise.

The main damage to human joints is the loss of cartilage which permits bones to slip smoothly on each other. Achieving similar lubrication is a major challenge in fitting synthetic joints. One approach is to inject collagen, a basic protein, which helps stimulate new growth of slippery tissue on the contact surface of the mechanical parts.

Arthritis is only one source of agonizing pain. No one knows exactly why pain hurts, but it has been controlled traditionally by drugs and opiates. In cases of terminal cancer and other severe chronic pain the only remedy has been severing the nerves that bear pain messages to the brain. Now man's artifice has been brought to bear upon this problem as well.

In 1962 Dr. Robert H. Pudenz and Dr. C. Hunter Shelden, Pasadena, California, neurosurgeons, tested an electronic device, known as a bioreceiver, planted in the central nervous system. It was tried on three persons suffering severe facial pain. The tiny radio receiver was planted in the skull with wires leading to the face nerves. When triggered by a transmitter outside the body, the device passed an electric current into the nerve, depolarizing it and easing the pain. Later the two doctors invented a more sophisticated instrument capable of controlling, stimulating, or blocking nerve messages. Smaller than a fifty-cent piece, the electronic package controls pain by impinging upon nerve fibers passing up the spinal cord to the brain. Impulses, triggered by a transmitter that the patient carries in a pocket, stimulate the nerves at rates up to 21,000 pulsations a second, blocking the pain.

"I like to think of this as an artificial nervous system," Dr. Pudenz said. "As far as we know, this will stimulate or block any part of the central nervous system." Adaptations might prevent epileptic seizures or control aggressive behavior by stimulating certain areas of the brain. By 1973 the neurosurgeons had installed the mechanical pain controllers in a number of patients. One woman, who had suffered excruciating general pain for many years, reported that after the operation she could reduce or eliminate pain for a number of hours by triggering the electronic vibrator for a few minutes.[14]

As with drugs, the prospect of electronic systems that can alter mood and personality is both hopeful and frightening. Beyond control of pain and epileptic seizure looms the technique of implanting electrodes in precise areas of the brain. An electrical impulse applied to these areas could evoke specific feelings, sensations, perceptions, and movement. A person so equipped could apply such stimuli to himself. With such an artificial aid a man or woman could turn off an emotion of unhappiness or despair with the flick of a switch. It would be possible to dial pleasure or delight and experience the ecstasy of sexual intercourse and orgasm without touching another human being.[15] In a society already oriented to the quest for instant happiness in drugs and pills, synthetic mood control could lead to degeneration rather than elevation of human morals and spirit. More frightening is the prospect that these devices, installed in large numbers of people, could be triggered by remote transmitters. A political dictator armed with such tools could manipulate large populations, holding people in docile subservience or arousing them to aggression against an enemy according to his personal wishes. By switching on occasional happiness and orgiastic delight, such a modern despot could wield mass control more effective than the bread and circuses of the Roman caesars. Such possibilities are chilling, but they demonstrate how rapidly science penetrates the realms of science fiction. If a device to ease pain can be used to destroy free will, then it is past time to ask if the human intellect is capable of rational and benevolent control of human inventions.

These may eventually extend to the use of small, portable computers to augment or control the brain. L. R. Pinneo, a computer scientist at the Stanford Research Institute in Menlo Park, California, reported that limb movement has been restored to paralyzed monkeys by electrodes planted in their brains. The Stanford work is aimed specifically toward helping people paralyzed by strokes.

"If many electrodes can be stimulated simultaneously and sequentially according to pattern, then coordinated limb movements and goal-directed behavior can be produced," Pinneo said. He emphasized that the experimental devices are still far from ready for human application. He visualizes that eventually the brain augmenter, or artificial brain, could be controlled by a miniaturized computer carried in the pocket.[16]

Other man-made parts and potions are less revolutionary. After twenty-five years of research pioneered during World War II, Dr. Robert P. Geyer, of Harvard University, announced in 1971 that synthetic blood is now a reality. The substance is a fat emulsion that can be injected directly into the bloodstream to supply food energy and emulsify chemical compounds. The key elements are fluorocarbons capable of absorbing oxygen and carbon dioxide and giving them off again. Dr. Geyer said he had replaced up to 90 percent of the natural blood in rats that continued to live normally and later regenerated their own blood. Fluorocarbons are a key ingredient in the operation of heart-lung machines while a patient is in surgery. The scientist believes doctors one day will be able to replace one half or more of natural human blood with the synthetic fluid. When practical, this would reduce the need for blood donors and emergency shipments of plasma to save the injured in a disaster.[17]

In October, 1954, the first human patient received a surgical blood-vessel graft made of nylon tubing developed by Chemstrand Corporation. The braided, crimped nylon tubing is used much in the same form today, although subsequent years have seen hundreds of technical teams developing new materials and shaped plastic parts to replace damaged blood vessels and heart valves. It is now common, in cases of advanced arteriosclerosis, to remove segments of the aorta and its branches and replace them with synthetic material. As early as 1962 surgeons replaced diseased mitral valves in the hearts of two patients with polyurethane plastic valves. Several types are now in use.

Plastic blood vessels and valves have been fairly effective, but some difficulties persist. One is the danger of blood clots, which can cause stroke. The other is damage to blood cells flowing across the synthetic part, leading to anemia. Blood-compatible coatings have been developed, and it may be possible to induce growth of new human tissue coatings within the artificial part. Vein and artery replacements were limited to the largest blood vessels until recent tests of a new plastic material, Electrolour, suitable for replacing vessels down to eight millimeters (about one-fourth inch) in diameter.[18]

Thousands of heart patients have been helped by the mechanical pacemaker, an implanted electrical device which stimulates regular pulsation in a faulty heart. By 1972 more than fifty thousand Americans were equipped with these, although they are still not perfect. One problem is packaging the pacemaker and its power source small enough to plant within the chest cavity without damaging other organs. Second is the necessity to operate again to replace batteries, which last only one or two years.

Dr. Michael Bilitch, professor at the University of Southern

California School of Medicine, found in 1971 that pacemakers removed from dead persons showed signs that many had not been functioning properly. Examination of 250 deceased patients showed that half of the devices had malfunctioned. A central registry of pacemaker recipients is now maintained to keep in touch with patients and check their condition by phone.[19] Also in 1971 it was discovered that external electromagnetic radiation may interfere with the sensitive mechanisms. U.S. Public Health officials warned that a pacemaker's action may be altered by signals from a nearby radio station, hospital electric equipment, automobile ignition systems, radar transmission, or some household appliances such as microwave ovens.[20]

To solve the battery problem, technicians have turned to the atom as a more reliable power source. In 1970 the first nuclear-powered heart pacemaker was implanted in a fifty-eight-year-old woman at Broussais Hospital in Paris by Dr. Paul Laurens and Dr. Armand H. Pivnica. The miniature system, as long as a fingernail and as wide as a cigarette, was attached to the inside of the woman's chest cavity above her diaphragm with wires imbedded in the heart muscle. Power produced by radioactive decay of 1/5,000 ounce of plutonium 238 will operate the pacemaker for ten years. The doctors said that 90 percent of the radiation from the plutonium cell is absorbed harmlessly by the tantalum and platinum sheath around the device. In a year the patient will receive no more damaging radiation than she would receive from one X ray.[21]

The main goal is an artificial heart that may be implanted complete with a reliable power source to keep it operating. A number of preliminary approaches have been made, but most have proved to be premature.

On April 4, 1969, Dr. Denton Cooley, the Houston heart surgeon, startled the world by planting an artificial heart in Haskell Karp, one of his patients. At that time Dr. Cooley had already transplanted nineteen human hearts. He said he installed the man-made pump in a last-ditch effort to keep Karp alive until a suitable human heart donor could be found. That did not happen until two days later.

On April 6 Dr. Cooley was notified of a woman dying of brain damage in Massachusetts. Although clinically dead, she was flown to Houston while her heart was sustained by stimulant drugs. The next morning, in a three-hour operation, Dr. Cooley removed Karp's artificial heart and replaced it with the live one. Karp died of pneumonia thirty-eight hours later, but the spectacular experiment proved one thing: The synthetic heart sustained life for sixty-five hours.

Aside from the ethical question of employing such drastic measures to sustain life for a few hours, Dr. Cooley's action stirred a storm of protest. It was claimed that the artificial heart had been pirated from Dr. Michael E. DeBakey, the other famous Houston heart surgeon, who had spent years developing heart valves and the artificial heart itself. Cooley claimed that he had developed his own with the assistance of Dr. Domingo Liotta, a former associate of DeBakey.[22] This tempest in the teapot of medical technology proved little except that the synthetic heart was still not ready to sustain human life on a long-term basis.

In 1967 Dr. DeBakey planted an artificial left ventricular bypass (half a heart) in a Mexican woman to assist her own heart in healing. Ten days later it was removed, and the woman recovered from her illness. Still stinging from the professional controversy, Dr. Cooley commented: "By the end of this decade we won't be letting people die on our tables. Some patients will live for a year with an artificial heart inside them."[23]

His words may have been truly prophetic. During the past decade the National Institutes of Health have poured millions of dollars of research funds into development of synthetic means to assist the heart and blood vessels. Some prototype hearts have been tried with more or less success.

Experimenters at Stanford Research Institute reported a system to beam power from an outside source into the body. This radiated power would be picked up by a tiny coil planted under the skin and transmitted by wire from there to a pacemaker or artificial heart. The device was tested in six animals for periods up to twelve months.[24]

Then, in March, 1972, two scientists from the National Heart and Lung Institute announced development of a totally implantable synthetic heart and a nuclear-powered assistant heart. Dr. Lowell T. Harmison, project chief, and Dr. Theodore Cooper, director of the institute, said the artificial heart had been tested successfully in seventy-five calves, though for periods of only two to ten days. The artificial heart is cylindrically shaped, is seven inches across, and weighs about six pounds. It can be operated by battery or possibly by nuclear power cells. Although the heart is still to be proved for human use, the animal tests indicate that a workable artificial heart is really in sight.[25]

Dr. Horst Klinkmann, East Germany's leading organ-transplant specialist, believes the artificial heart will be available in clinics within five years. He sees the day when a man with a bad heart will be able to drop it off at a clinic for repairs while he goes about his business fitted with an artificial substitute. Dr. Klinkmann's optimism is based on the fact that the heart is a muscle and not a complicated biochemical organ such as the liver or kidneys. The great advantage to the mechanical heart is that it will allow doctors to remove the natural heart, freeze it, and make necessary repairs. "In two-thirds of the cases, the original heart could be returned after it was repaired," he said. "In the other one-third, the people could survive with artificial hearts in their bodies."[26]

It will be longer before serious thought can be given the possibility of implanting artificial kidneys, lungs, liver, or organs of the endocrine system. In the meantime machines to help the body from the outside are being improved steadily. Dr. A. J. Lande, a New York surgeon, told the American Thoracic Society that blood oxygenators (heart-lung machines) "have come of age." Whereas early machines could be used for only a few hours because of blood-cell damage, modern heart-lung machines have been used with animals up to sixteen days, and ten days with human patients. With advanced blood circulation systems, Dr. Lande explained, it may now become possible to keep patients alive long enough for sick lungs to heal or for antibiotics to cure acute pneumonia.[27]

Replacing the liver is possibly the most complex medical problem of all. Scientists have estimated it would require a plant larger than a house to perform the functions of this remarkable chemical-processing factory. Fortunately, of all body organisms, the liver enjoys the highest ability to regenerate its cells. Therefore, while the liver transplant progresses to the stage of standard operation, its task can be done temporarily by perfusing the blood through another liver, such as a pig's. This is the nearest we have yet come to an artificial liver.

Equally remote is the true artificial brain, though not as remote as it might seem. Brain cells do not duplicate themselves after birth, and a large number die each day, but nature gave us excess mental capacity, and there exists the possibility of grafting nerve tissue from another brain. Future computer technology may also be applied, in addition to the Stanford development already noted. Dr. Huberto Fernandez-Moran, professor of biophysics at the University of Chicago, told the New York Academy of Sciences that computer memory components may someday be made as small as cells of the brain:

> Man's most efficient ultra-miniaturized information storage and retrieval system—the memory portion of the brain—has a packing density of about one billion elements per cubic inch. By printing electronic circuits on high resolution films and electro-optically reducing them, we can already manufacture integrated micro-electronic systems with packing densities of more than 100,000 elements per cubic inch. Eventually it should be possible to fabricate sub-micron, ultra-miniaturized circuits which approach macromolecular dimensions.[28]

In other words, when computer memory bits can be made as small as molecules, we may be able to plug new memory banks into our brain at will.

This is unlikely to come in time to aid failing memories of today's octogenarians, but the computer may assist in another way. Researchers at the Institute for the Future at Middletown, Connecticut, predict that by the year 2000 we will see a demonstration of man-machine symbiosis enabling a man to extend his intelligence by direct electromechanical interaction between his brain and a computing machine, bypassing the senses through which we normally receive information.[29] The same suggestion was made by Dr. Glenn T. Seaborg, former chairman of the Atomic Energy Commission:

> If it were possible to make a direct connection between brain and computer so people could learn during sleep, we could produce a mankind that would be able to solve all the physical and social problems that the human race faces today. Of course, I do not overlook the danger of the wrong information being programmed into human beings. But then we do that today, without the help of computers.[30]

Another suggested human change to cope with our polluted world came from Dr. Irvin J. Selikoff, director of the Environmental Services Laboratory at Mt. Sinai School of Medicine, New York. He believes the lining of the respiratory tract might be altered, perhaps by biochemical techniques, to make it sensitive to certain harmful pollutants in the air, then "each person could become his own air pollution station."[31]

"The biological bombshells to come will be quicker-acting and more stunning than their physical forerunners," predicted Desmond King-Hele, British space scientist. "The transplanting of hearts, lungs, and kidneys may lead on to man-robot hybrids or disembodied brains kept going on heart-lung machines."[32]

The phrase "man-robot hybrid" arouses an uneasy feeling that perhaps we are going too far in the application of machines and synthetic parts to extend human capabilities, but this has been going on for a long time. The airplane, automobile, computers, radar—even the telephone—all are mechanical extensions of our senses and manipulatory powers. Hundreds of others we accept matter-of-factly in everyday life, and the technology of cybernetics is devoted to the concept of bringing man and machine ever closer. Remotely controlled hands, developed for handling radioactive materials behind protective shielding, is one example of a cybernetic device, a term that means the organic fusion of the human organism with active machine components.

"Instead of using external or attached prosthetic devices," said Manfred Clynes, author of *Evolution of the Superman*, "the man-made devices are now to be incorporated into the regulatory feedback chains—the homeostatic mechanisms that keep us viable for such an astonishingly long time."[33]

The key word is "feedback." It means that a human operator —of a mechanical arm or total machine—receives signals back from an action to signify what the machine is doing and, from this information, determines what the next motion is to be. An example would be artificial fingers that could sense heat and signal the brain to pull the hand away from the fire.

On a larger scale some machines now place a *man* within *them*, not just as operator but as an integral part of the machine itself. One of these, developed by General Electric Company, is called CAMS (for Cybernetic Anthropomorphous Machine System). The robot is eleven feet tall and weighs three thousand pounds. It is four-footed, with articulated knees, and moves at five miles an hour on aluminum legs. In demonstrations its human "component" was Ralph S. Mosher, the General Electric engineer who designed it. At the controls, linked to a force feedback system, he could "feel" when the machine's feet touched the ground or an object. CAMS can lift a 500-pound load, scatter a stack of 175-pound beams, or put its foot down on an egg without breaking it.[34]

So we can approach the concept of artificial man either by replacing human parts until the natural body is totally renewed or by assembling a machine and placing it under feed-back human control.

The ultimate extension of human power—a concept of the late Dandridge Cole, who died while planning advanced space-exploration systems for General Electric—is a disembodied human brain planted within a powerful machine. It is conceivable that this final artificial mutation of man could produce work heretofore unheard-of. Probably "he" or "it" could travel to the stars.

This biomachine might even approach immortality, the long dream, but despite the human brain, it would be human no longer.

PART III

Keys to
the Kingdom

CHAPTER 7

What Is
Life?

"What is life?" is a question that has stimulated an unending stream of inanities and profundities from earliest days to the present. Every important philosopher, scientist, theologian, and politician has pondered and tried an answer. Yet it has never been answered completely, and some believe it will never be.

Only two other questions are more difficult: "How?" and "Why?"

Ever since Eve plucked the apple and Adam found it infected with the worm of hard work we have been clambering around the tree of knowledge, picking more apples in search of final answers. We have accumulated a cellarful of answers, but the most elusive apples still dangle beyond reach in the high branches. Tomorrow we may know it all; today we are still searching.

Why is it so difficult? We know life when we see it. A flower is alive; a thistle is alive. An elephant lives, and so do the mites and insects that infest its thick gray hide.

A man lives; a mountain does not. A child knows kinship

with a kitten, not with a rock. But the same soup of chemicals made it all—lions and stone, peacocks and sand, men and dust.

We cannot come quite yet to a materialistic definition of the elusive spark that bridges the dimensions between a living and a dead thing, but we can enumerate the characteristics of the living. A live thing eats and converts food to growth. It reproduces its kind. It is irritable, in the sense that it responds to stimuli such as light, heat, or touch. It moves (even the oldest tree root) and adapts to environmental change. Inanimate objects also can do some of these things. A weathervane shifts with the wind, and water turns to ice, but a living organism performs all the activities of life at one time or another. No nonliving thing can do them all.

This differentiation takes us only *that* close to the mystery of creation. Biologists have bored down and down with ultra-centrifuges, electron microscopes, and gas chromatoscopes to the basic cell. Within its infinitesimal skin they have found an amazing computerized factory equipped with the knowledge of all ages of evolution. But we have not yet seen that moment of ultimate decision when atoms link together in the special shimmering beauty of a molecule complete, mobile, self-replicating, only a split second of space-time removed from a brother molecule which does *not* come alive.

We do not comprehend how death comes to life, or life comes to death. What is the ultimate difference when a man is dead and the vibrant lamps of a thousand trillion cells wink out one by one? Above all, we do not understand why the mind of man is driven to find the core of his source. Is it this curiosity, the special mark of *our* kind of life, that finally becomes the undeniable clue that our life originated beyond the natural confines of earth?

In a sense it would be disappointing to learn that our noblest urges of quest had been aimed no higher than to prove the Bible wrong. The wisest biologist, chemist, or physicist feels the shadow of God at his elbow. Each time he discovers a new and deeper cause, he runs the risk that his next discovery may be the First Cause itself. This is the possibility that tantalizes our deepest dreams. At that moment will we find God or only the end (or the beginning?) of man?

This sort of cosmic stage fright set inhibiting brakes on biological science for many centuries. The architectural subtlety and chemical complexity presented by a single living cell—let alone the billions of cooperating cells that make up a man—are so immense that the fainthearted may be pardoned for rationalizing his failure to comprehend. In the history of biology this rationalization frequently expressed itself as "vitalism," the doctrine that life operates through mysterious forces, residing in the cell or elsewhere, that would forever elude explanation. This doctrine smothered the advance of biology at least until 1900, and some traces may persist today. However, the past twenty years have seen a biological revolution refreshing as a crocus bursting through the last snow of spring. We now see the patterns upon which life is built.

The ancients believed in abiogenesis, the theory that lower forms of life are born from nonliving matter. Aristotle taught the doctrine of spontaneous generation. He accepted as fact that maggots sprang from decaying matter, plant lice were born in the dew of morning, and worms came from cheese and wood.[1] It wasn't until two thousand years later that the Renaissance bred men with method and courage to contradict the master.

First was the Italian biologist Francesco Redi. In 1668 he exposed meat in jars, some open, others covered with gauze. As the meat decayed, maggots appeared in the uncovered jars, but only on top of the gauze covering the others. Where flies could lay no eggs, no maggots could be born.[2]

That settled the question for a time, but it was aroused again when scientists became aware of microorganisms. The theory of spontaneous generation shifted down to these previously invisible entities. In the 1700's the Italian abbé Lazzaro Spallanzini showed that not even microscopic organisms could develop in a broth that was sealed off from the air and boiled, but the doubters persisted. They claimed boiling changed the air so it would no longer generate new life.

Louis Pasteur in 1860 finally laid the old theory to rest with a modification of Spallanzini's experiment. Instead of sealing the broth, he drew the neck of the flask into an S-shaped curve. Fresh air entered the flask, but heavier particles of dust, bacteria, and mold were trapped in the curve of the neck before reaching the broth. Pasteur boiled it. No organisms appeared.[3]

Most scientists then accepted the conclusion that all life must come from other life. As far as we know, this may be true, but it leaves the question of how, when, and where it happened for the first time. A form of the theory that life *did* arise spontaneously, or by chance, is still much alive today, though hammered into new shapes since Aristotle.

Three great clarifying waves of thought have washed across the life sciences in the past 150 years.

The first, dating from the 1830's, was the recognition that all living organisms are composed of cells and that life and growth are functions of cell division.

The second was the theory of evolution, conceived independently by Charles Darwin and Alfred Wallace and announced in 1858. Many scientists regard Darwin's work as biology's most profound theoretical achievement. He concluded that all life has evolved from lower forms, each stepping up by natural selection and mutation so that the strongest, or best-adapted, specimens lived to transmit their strength or special talent to the next generation.

The third unifying discovery was the work of Gregor Mendel, an Austrian monk. His mathematical description of the basic principles of heredity was published in an obscure journal in 1865, though it was lost or ignored by scientists until 1900.[4]

So we have the cell (a thousand could dance on the head of a pin), evolution (our ancestors were slime in the primordial ocean), and heredity (the shape of a father is passed to the son), all bursting upon the human intellect in a short span of thirty-five years in the nineteenth century, one flashing moment in the clock of eternity. They have channeled the thought of the past hundred years.

The cell itself has absorbed the intellectual energies of a thousand brilliant men. We now accept without question that the single cell is the basis of all life. Some creatures, such as bacteria or amoebas, have only one. Others, such as men, contain trillions. At some moment in the womb cells are instructed to take different shapes, then multiply. From the blood of a mother, who is hardly aware of their existence, the cells feed and move to their work. Some become blood, others bone. Some make a liver and others a heart. Some create that special tissue, the egg factories, which insures that the next of the species will be born.

Some cells, such as the egg of certain creatures, measure several inches across. Most are so small that four thousand together would not fill an inch. Bacteria cells may be round, spiral, or rod-shaped. Skin cells of a leaf are thick-walled cubes. Other leaf cells are long and rectangular and contain masses of green coloring matter. Yeast cells are spherical.

Animals contain many special cells. Those in muscle are long and pointed. Skin cells are thin and flat. Those in the brain and nerves have branched tendrils like tree roots. Red blood corpuscles are normally shaped like disks, whereas the white ones vary in shape and move like amoebas. Inside the cell is a nucleus where its government resides, surrounded by cytoplasm, long considered the basic stuff of life.[5]

That description of a living cell, however, is too simple. When investigators with infinite patience dissected this minute organism, they found chromosomes, nucleoli, mitochondria, lysosomes, endoplasmic reticulum, ribosomes, centrosomes, and the Golgi body: strange names for things never named before, some linked to their discoverers, others designating function in terms comprehensible to scientists of all nations.

Inside the cell we found a self-contained, self-regulated manufacturing plant maintaining its own life, determining its own moment of death, and operating the machinery to make another exactly like itself. In this exquisite factory the mitochondria serve as power plants, storing and releasing energy in molecular reactions. Lysosomes dismantle the cell when its usefulness is ended. The endoplasmic reticulum is a convoluted inner membrane with guidance and control functions. On this are clustered the ribosomes, tiny granular operators which synthesize protein. Other functions remain under study. Enveloping everything is the cell membrane, the factory wall which protects the inner works, pumps materials in or out, and acts as a sensory apparatus.[6]

The cell converts water, fat, carbohydrate, and protein into the energy that keeps our body operating. The cell also sets into motion the intricate process, known as mitosis, by which it divides into two daughter cells, each containing computer and operating equipment identical to the original. A special process is involved in dividing the cells of sexual reproduction. This is meiosis, or reduction division, in which four (instead of two) new cells are formed, each containing only half of the information needed to make a new creature. The other half, by ancient wisdom, will come when the sex cell combines with a stranger in whatever form of intercourse nature has decreed to fashion a new being.[7]

Cells may be killed by work or by accident (such as nuclear radiation). In a man billions die, and billions more are born every minute. In the blood alone three to ten million new red cells are created in the bone marrow each second while others die to be disposed of in the spleen.[8] When it is done with its work, the cell determines its moment of death. A red blood cell lives about twenty days. Why this long and no longer? We don't know—yet.

Until 1898 it was thought that bacteria were the smallest living creatures, but then Martinus Willem Beijerinck, a Dutch botanist, found something smaller that could cause disease. He isolated what he thought was a fluid which harmed tobacco plants and named it virus, Latin for "poison."

In 1935 Wendell Stanley, an American biochemist, verified that viruses are solid particles containing protein. Most are so tiny that only the electron microscope reveals them. We now know they consist of a central core of nucleic acid surrounded by a protein coat. Viruses are generally accepted as the missing link between living and nonliving matter because they appear to be both dead and alive. They are so incomplete that they appear dead until they attach themselves to a living cell as parasites. Then the core of the virus bores through the cell membrane, takes over the cell's life processes, and uses the cell's substance to reproduce more virus.[9] The unpleasant consequence of this high-handed piracy is a virus disease.

Examination of this link between living and nonliving particles concentrates attention on protein. That word conjures up healthy food such as steak, fish, and eggs. In our overfed culture most of us have been told that we need more protein, less fats and sugar. In other nations, where billions live at the edge of malnutrition, lack of protein causes disease, stunted growth, and mental deficiency. Protein is the basic building block, but the number of *different* protein molecules may approach infinity.

Fats, carbohydrates, and proteins are the principal constituents of living matter, and proteins are the most important. They represent nearly one half of the body's dry matter (70 percent is water). One kind, myosin, forms the contractile fibers which enable us to move our muscles. Bones and cartilage are made of the protein collagen. The skin protein keratin protects our inner tissues against external attack. Some hormones are proteins, as are antibodies in the blood which defend us against viruses, which also are protein. There are proteins that stimulate others to work and finally those that carry the fundamental code of life. Protein molecules are much tinier than a cell, yet in their submicroscopic world they are monsters. Protein is a building block made of thousands of building blocks.

To gain a hint of protein's complexity, we might watch a modern biochemist perform a piece of research. First he must destroy a cell with a solvent. This releases many proteins, and he wishes to know the molecular weight of a single one. He uses an ingenious device known as the ultra-centrifuge developed by The Svedberg, a Swedish physical chemist. The many proteins are spun in this at speeds up to 70,000 revolutions per minute, centrifugal force equaling 400,000 times the force of gravity. Protein molecules move out from the center according to their relative size. An optical apparatus measures the rate of this molecular sedimentation, and weight can be calculated.

The *smallest* known protein has a molecular weight of 13,000, that many times heavier than a hydrogen atom, which is the lightest in the table of elements. Larger proteins range up to molecular weights of 10,000,000. Another way to look at it is to compare proteins with more common molecules. One of water, for example, contains two atoms of hydrogen and one of oxygen (H_2O). By comparison, the milk protein lactoglobulin has a molecular weight of 42,000. It contains 1,864 atoms of carbon, 3,012 of hydrogen, 576 of oxygen, 468 of nitrogen, and 21 of sulfur. The formula for that is written $C_{1864}H_{3012}O_{576}N_{468}S_{21}$. Determining the structure of proteins is not an exercise for a high-school chemistry class.

It might have remained impossible to build an accurate model of a protein molecule except for the discovery that they are made of smaller molecules, the amino acids. There are only about twenty amino acids, which simplifies the problem somewhat. Then the trick is to learn *how* they are linked together in different structures to build specific proteins.

Scientists have learned some of the rules by which the amino acids are linked by peptide bonds to form the molecules. It is these bonds that are broken when an organism dies.[10] The most spectacular proteins of all are the enzymes. The word may be associated in most minds with laundry detergent ballyhooed on television, but enzymes are more important than that. They are the catalytic whips, the slave-driver to every chemical process in the body's metabolism.

Cells die and are renewed at startling speeds. The entire red-cell population is replaced every three months. This rapid molecular turnover goes on in connective tissue, tendons and ligaments, blood-vessel walls, muscles, and fat. Swift changes occur even in the bones as links of molecular chains are split and welded again in the ceaseless round of metabolism.

How this happens was a puzzle because most biochemical reactions do not take place spontaneously. When body processes are tested in laboratory glassware, most chemicals of life combine or decompose much more slowly than the pace observed in real life. The average protein must be boiled for twenty-four hours in a solution of hydrochloric acid to be broken down. The body does the same thing in four hours or less, *without* high temperatures or strong acids.

The difference lies in the enzymes which speed up chemical reactions without being changed themselves. They are destroyed only by wear and tear or poisoning, and they work in extremely small concentrations. The factory where a single cell conducts 1,000 to 2,000 chemical reactions requires only about 100,000 enzyme molecules to accelerate all the functions. A single molecule of the enzyme that splits hydrogen peroxide into water and oxygen (and creates white foam when the antiseptic is placed on a wound) can transform 5,000,000 peroxide molecules a minute.

These biochemical middlemen—the first of which was isolated in 1926—play a significant part in every vital process. They help plants build tissue, turn leaves red and yellow in the fall, make the cut surface of an apple or potato turn brown, convert grape juice into wine, and grain mash into whiskey. The living organism appears to manufacture a specific enzyme to do each of thousands of different jobs. Enzymes "know" when to act and when not to and star in the most elemental drama of all, the beginning of new life.

An unfertilized egg as it leaves the female ovary is loaded with structural materials and hundreds of enzymes to engineer the building of a new human being from a tiny blob of protoplasm. The enzymes, however, are blocked until the egg is fertilized. Then, and only then, hundreds of reactions are set off at once, and the cell begins to grow and divide.

Before that, an even older male-female drama of aggression and resistance is enacted on the infinitesimal stage. The unfertilized egg is protected by a tough coating of cells cemented with a substance called hyaluronic acid. (The lady has her door locked.) The spermatozoa who woo her are already handicapped and weary from their long swim upstream in the vaginal canal and into the uterus, where the coy lady-egg waits. Millions of their brothers have given up the struggle by now, but the strongest drive on, and the lady will accept nothing less.

When a sperm cell reaches the locked shell, he carries a secret weapon, the enzyme hyaluronidase, designed specifically to shatter the barrier and permit his penetration. But now nature, which designed this game of life like a fairy tale of prince and princess, throws one more obstacle in the path to test his strength and perseverance. At the wall the sperm cell discovers he does not have enough enzyme to break through by himself, but there remains one more ploy. Our sperm prince is not alone at the castle wall. Other princes have survived the final courtship of the lady; there are perhaps thousands at the stout barricade. So the strongest prince borrows enzymes from his rivals, penetrates the wall, and wins the lady's hand in marriage. Presumably they live happily ever after in the trillions of cells of a new being.

We're not quite sure how he borrows enzyme from his rivals, but it helps explain why nature seems to waste millions of sperm cells to achieve a single egg fertilization. A shortage of this enzyme may be the reason some people are sterile. Physicians have administered extra quantities of hyaluronidase to some people, enabling them to have children. Some vitamins are a part of the enzyme mechanism, and some drugs work to cure disease by denying enzymes to the germs.[11] Understanding enzymes and how they work is profoundly important to medicine and pharmacology. Scientists may be able not only to isolate and use enzymes from the body, but to make new ones for any particular desired reaction. Hundreds of industrial processes of the future are likely to be based upon enzyme action.

These molecular catalysts take us very close to the basic mechanisms of life, but not quite to the source. That quest returns us to a modern version of spontaneous generation, the theory that somewhere, sometime, there was a magic moment when enough thousands of carbon, hydrogen, oxygen, and nitrogen atoms bumped together and latched into a long-chain molecule, which "saw it was good" and made a replica of itself. This would have been the primeval germ of the millions of life forms which have inhabited earth since that moment billions of years ago. That would have been the creation of order out of chaos.

How would that first organic molecule recognize the arrival of the final atom which made it complete and alive? How could a process that requires enzymes happen without the first enzyme? What would such a molecule "know" about the acquisition and use of energy required for reproduction? These are some of the questions lying at that ever-shifting boundary between human knowledge and the First Cause.

Life might have arrived on mold spores or viruses from outer space. That possibility, however, only pushes the origin somewhere else. So scientists have built a logical litany to bolster the theory that we came to be by random chance. It is difficult to imagine that a beautiful girl running down a sandy beach happened by chance, but in our narrow span of existence we cannot comprehend the billions of years "chance" has had to perform its work. Given the universe as we see it (and that's a great deal to give without asking the source), scientists postulate that nothing is impossible. That smacks of an older thought named "miracle," but let's follow it through. Given the billions of years past and those to come, plus the forces of the universe, many of which remain unknown, I can believe that sometime, somehow, those forces might group themselves in the special arrangement needed to float my typewriter in midair or turn it into a carrot. It is not likely either would happen in a moment, but it might possibly occur given enough energy, space, and time.

This is the sort of mental gymnastic required to accept the random creation of life. The theory goes that the old seas were a rich hot soup of chemical elements with atoms constantly in motion, bumping into each other, frolicking under the warm outpouring of energy from the sun. There were no creatures to cause decay, nor free oxygen to hasten the process, so molecules would have enjoyed millions of years without interference to try random combinations until the right one came along. Then one day a mass of loosely connected atoms, basking under the primeval sun, might have been struck by a bolt of lightning or a cosmic ray from a distant star—and there was life. We won't ask who sent the cosmic ray or lightning or the sunshine, but we might be pardoned for wondering if that first massive molecule knew it was alive. It seems only fitting that self-awareness should have been present that first lovely moment, else it becomes difficult to locate the gene that gave us a brain which prompts us to ask the question.

This theory of spontaneous generation seems either contrived or logical depending upon the individual point of view. As stated by George Wald, former professor of biology at Harvard:

> In such a problem as the spontaneous origin of life, we have no way of assessing probabilities beforehand, or even of deciding what we mean by a trial. The origin of a living organism is undoubtedly a stepwise phenomenon, each step with its own probability and conditions of trial.
>
> The important point is that since the origin of life belongs in the category of at-least-once phenomena, time is on its side. However improbable we regard this event, or any of the steps which it involves, given enough time it will almost certainly happen at least once. And for life as we know it, with its capacity for growth and reproduction, once may be enough.
>
> Time is in fact the hero of the plot. The time with which we have to deal is of the order of two billion years. What we re-

gard as impossible on the basis of human experience is meaningless here. Given so much time, the impossible becomes possible, the possible probable, and the probable virtually certain. One has only to wait; time itself performs the miracles.[12]

One time-honored test of a miracle or a theory is to see if men can reproduce it. As early as the 1950's Harold Urey, Nobel laureate in chemistry, became interested in the degree to which electrical discharges in the upper atmosphere might promote the formation of organic compounds. One of his students, S. L. Miller, circulated a mixture of water vapor, methane, ammonia, and hydrogen—all gases believed to have been present in the atmosphere of early earth—continuously for a week over an electric spark. At the end of the week the water was analyzed. To their surprise, Urey and Miller found amino acids, glycine, and alanine. Amino acids make protein. Protein makes men.[13]

"Many laboratory studies have shown that under the conditions presumed to have existed on the primitive earth, most of the molecules essential to life could have come into existence spontaneously," commented Sidney Fox, of the University of Miami. "But the living organism appears to be far more than a simple assembly of such building blocks."

Professor Fox reported on experiments with mixtures similar to the primordial atmosphere. He concluded that the actions forming large molecules are *not random*, that the tendency to do this preexists in the atoms and smaller molecules. He defines life not as creating order out of disorder, but as converting a degree of order to a higher level, or converting one kind of order to other kinds at other levels. The formation of large molecules then is still not the beginning.[14]

Coming to understand remains our present condition. Professor Fox indicates what others, too, have found: that no matter how far we dig into the molecules and atoms, we continue to find evidence of preexisting order rather than random chance.

We also have found the core of life and the code to that.

CHAPTER 8

The Core
and the Code

Peas growing in a serene monastery garden of Austria more than one hundred years ago provided a key to the core and code that transmit the continuity of life forms through all generations. That key lay hidden, forgotten, and rusty from disuse for many years, but in our time it is unlocking the basic secrets of life.

We look at a newborn child and say: "He has his mother's eyes," or "That nose is just like his father's." We know by instinct or vague knowledge that the "bloodline" of a family carries with it certain traits transmitted from grandfather to father to son, modified by new "blood" supplied by husbands and wives found in faraway places. Such words as "gene" and "chromosome" have found their way into the common language to designate the mysterious mechanisms by which a virus or a pea or a tree or a man inherits physical (and in the latter case, mental) characteristics.

Such words did not exist in the day of Gregor Johann Mendel. He was born in 1822 in Heinzendorf, part of Austrian Silesia. Natural science interested him, but he followed a more

traditional profession. Mendel entered the Augustinian monastery at Brunn and was ordained a priest in 1847. During
monastic training he taught himself some science, taught
youngsters Greek and mathematics, and then was sent to the
University of Vienna, where he studied physics, chemistry,
math, zoology, and botany.

Mendel also experimented. Beginning in 1856, with only a
monastery garden as his laboratory, he began planting and
crossbreeding peas. For more than ten years he followed the
course of patient experiments, observing the regularity with
which traits of crossbred plants could be expected to reappear
in succeeding generations. From this he defined the mathematical proportions in which hereditary characteristics are
transmitted and deduced that these were carried from one generation to the next by paired elements, which we now know as
genes. The ratios which he worked out between dominant and
recessive traits passing through the generations came eventually to be known as Mendel's laws. Time proved their applica-
bility to fleas as well as horses, plants, and men.

Without knowing about Darwin's contemporary work on
evolution, Mendel reported his findings to the Natural Science
Society of Brunn. This group published his report in 1866.
There Mendel's laws went to sleep for a third of a century.
After a few more plant experiments, which did not turn out so
well, Mendel was named abbot of his monastery in 1868. His
final sixteen years were spent in administrative duties and
arguing with the Austrian government over monastery taxes.[1]

It's a plaintive little tale, this story of a brilliant man growing peas in a monastery garden. In another time and place he
might have burned at the Inquisition's stake for audacity or
certainly would have won the grandfather of Nobel prizes. He
was a seeker of pure knowledge, and he found it with little
guidance from elsewhere.

Four years after Mendel's report in Brunn, Friedrich Miescher, of Tubingen, discovered a new chemical substance in
the nucleus of pus cells and later in fish sperm. This substance,

which he called nuclein, was deoxyribonucleic acid, now commonly known as DNA, core of the organic cell. Neither man knew the other. If they had, their work could have been coordinated and expanded. The two discoveries belonged together, but it would be seventy-five years more before the genetic significance of DNA would be based on anything more substantial than argument.

It is more remarkable that both Mendel and Miescher worked without knowing the process of egg fertilization, which begins all sexually reproduced organisms. In 1875 Oskar Hertwig for the first time observed the essentials of fertilization—in the sea urchin. This organism spawns small transparent eggs in seawater where a sperm enters an egg. After penetration the sperm's nucleus swells up to an appearance similar to the nucleus of the egg. The two then coalesce into a single unit. It was soon confirmed in both animals and plants that fertilization consists of the complete union of two, and only two, sexual cells, and it involves the union of the two parental cell nuclei.[2]

The years hatched many other theories concerning cell division and heredity, but the Mendelian laws, which were ahead of the main currents of knowledge, were not rediscovered until 1900. That year three men, working independently, all came up with the answers Mendel had found thirty-five years earlier. They were Hugo De Vries in Holland, Carl Correns in Germany, and Erich von Tschermak in Austria. They relighted a candle that had sputtered out before it could give light. The relighted candle set off others like strings of firecrackers, opening the realm of molecular biology.

By 1900 many scientists suspected that genetic information was hidden inside pairs of tiny, threadlike strands in cell nuclei. These threads were called chromosomes, or colored bodies, because of their ability to absorb dye and become visible under the microscope. The view inside the nucleus was still muddied by a confusion of protein and other compounds. Students scanning the inner structure could see that the chromosomes, during cell division, always split lengthwise, giving each daughter cell an equal share of what was presumed to be hereditary material.

Seeking the message in the egg ran counter to the view held by most biologists up to Darwin and beyond. The early ones believed the germ cells received their information from the rest of the body. Darwin conceived of each organ sending out particles into the bloodstream. These then were assembled into egg and sperm. This view would have supported the misguided theories of Lysenko in Russia, who built a body of dogma to show that characteristics acquired from the environment (including Communist doctrine) could be transmitted by heredity. Now, with the chromosomes in view, it became evident that the organs of the body do not reorder their own kind, but depend for creation upon the coded information carried in the heart of each cell from its hereditary past.

This was essentially proved by Thomas Hunt Morgan in the "fly room" at Columbia University. In 1909 Morgan began experimenting with common fruit flies, which swarm around any garbage can. His fly room, jammed with milk bottles containing fly colonies, became famous among his students. By many experiments with natural and induced mutations and ingenious crossbreeding, Morgan not only pinned down the chromosomes but also was able to "map" the relative positions of genes, the message carriers, along the insect's four pairs of chromosomes.[3] (By comparison, the human being has twenty-three pairs of chromosomes.)

The gene's physical nature still remained a mystery. The link had not yet been made with Miescher's DNA discovered a half century before. But by the 1940's molecular biologists had entered the arena to prove their contention that fundamental life processes could be fully understood on the molecular level. Their tools included the electron microscope and X-ray crystallography, a technique for deducing a molecule's structure by taking X-ray photographs of it from different angles.

The code bearer was finally pinned down like a butterfly by

the bacteriologist Oswald T. Avery at the Rockefeller Institute. Taking purified DNA extracted from the chromosomes of dead pneumonia bacteria, Avery and his associates showed that it could transform harmless bacteria into virulent ones. This elegant experiment showed that it was DNA that carried the genetic message. Confirmation came from other experiments that proved that the DNA of a virus could take over a germ and replace the cell's genetic instructions with its own. Only then was DNA accepted as the fabulous substance of the genes.[4]

The caldron of the life sciences bubbled with names of brilliance and genius. Sewell Wright, a patriarch of population genetics, had shown at the University of Chicago that by suitable breeding he could restore the fifth toe that guinea pigs had lost millions of years ago. Hermann J. Muller worked as a student under Morgan to establish modern genetics in the 1910–1915 period. Alfred H. Sturtevant developed a technique for mapping chromosomes in 1913. George W. Beadle demonstrated that genes govern cell chemistry. In 1946 he succeeded Morgan as head of biology at California Institute of Technology, one of the great centers of the life sciences. He also shared a Nobel Prize in 1958 with Edward L. Tatum and Joshua Lederberg. Lederberg, one of the most eminent biologists of this generation, discovered sexuality in bacteria. He is now at Stanford University.

Max Delbruck shifted from theoretical physics in Germany to analysis of gene mutations as atomic events. At Cal Tech he was greatly responsible for establishing the dogma that DNA is at the heart of life. Alfred D. Hershey also supported the DNA theory at the Carnegie Institution, Cold Spring Harbor, Long Island. Arthur Kornberg, an M.D. who became a biochemist, shared a Nobel Prize for the first production of DNA molecules outside the living cell. Seymour Benzer studied at Cal Tech and elsewhere and is noted for his work at Purdue University in mapping the DNA molecules that control functioning of viruses. Linus Pauling, one of the great chemists, had revealed the structure of protein molecules and in the early 1950's was at the verge of discovering the structure of DNA.[5]

These are only a few of the illustrious names involved in unwinding the strands at the heart of life. Some of them are still with us, still searching and still finding.

At mid-century some skepticism persisted, but it was generally accepted that the nucleic acid DNA was the final source of instruction for building a new cell and a new organism. Scientists knew the molecule was composed of phosphate, a sugar called deoxyribose, and chemical compounds called bases. These elements repeated thousands of times to form long, coiled chains. Chemists had also determined that the DNA bases were adenine, guanine, thymine, and cytosine, better known as A, G, T, and C. What they did not know was how this molecular code carrier was put together and how it worked.

To put the problem in size perspective, if all the DNA strands in a single human egg nucleus were separated and strung together, they would form a thread about five feet long but less than 1/10,000,000 of an inch in diameter. If folded back and forth to form a sheet one molecule thick, it would cover only 1/200 of the head of a pin. If all the DNA in all the egg cells that gave birth to the world's 3,700,000,000 people were corded together, it would fit inside a box only 1/8 inch square.[6]

Many skilled scientists were now probing into this submicroscopic world, but it was left to two relatively unknown men in England to unravel the secret. In 1953 Francis H. C. Crick, thirty-six, and James D. Watson, twenty-four, were working together at Cambridge University's Cavendish Laboratory. Crick was a physicist turned biologist. Watson had taken a Ph.D. in biology at Indiana University. How their lives entwined is almost as fascinating as the DNA master molecule, but in brief, after two relatively short years of work, their knowledge and inspiration combined to solve the structural problem. As they worked in their laboratory they built a model out of wire and metal parts like a tower of tinker toys. It was as revolutionary as models built almost a half century earlier to show the structure of simple atoms.

Exalted by the culmination of their labor, the two young men hurried out in the late winter afternoon to the Eagle, a pub where Cambridge scientists met to gossip about experiments and celebrate triumphs. Crick's booming voice drew a crowd of curious friends. "We have discovered the secret of life!" he announced proudly.[7]

In a sense they had. The concept that Watson and Crick had translated into a visible model showed that the long DNA molecule is composed of two threads loosely entwined around each other in a double helix like a long spiral staircase. The strands were held apart (rather, linked together) at thousands of points, like steps in the stairs, by pairs of chemical bases, joined at the center by hydrogen atoms. The stairsteps, each made of two sections, with adenine (A) paired with thymine (T), and cytosine (C) paired with guanine (G), comprise the bits of information in the genetic code. The long threads and their connecting stairsteps are arranged head to tail so that one half of the DNA molecule becomes a mirror image of the other. One strand read from top to bottom is the same as the other read from bottom to top. When a cell divides, the molecule untwists and unzips down the middle as though a carpenter were to saw through the stairsteps from top to bottom. Each half then finds additional materials in the chemical soup of the cell nucleus to form another like the original. In this fashion all the information in the genetic code is passed on to each new cell.

Proof of the concept came in 1956 from Arthur Kornberg, then at Washington University in St. Louis. He discovered an enzyme (named DNA polymerase) that was critical to the workings of the double helix. After obtaining a sufficient quantity of the enzyme, Kornberg placed a piece of incomplete DNA in a test tube with a mixture of the proper chemical fragments. The incomplete DNA picked up its complementary pieces (nucleotides) from the chemicals and completed itself, confirming the Watson-Crick theory.

That proved one function. The other question was: How does DNA direct the construction of protein molecules to build all the parts of an organism, such as a human being? What exactly is the code, and how is it transmitted from the DNA into the cytoplasm of the cell?

The tiny bits of A, T, C, and G lining the thread of unzipped DNA are like a single row of braille. A DNA strand then may be thought of as a long "sentence" whose phrases (the genes) are formed of "words" spelled with only four different "letters"—the stairstep bases. At first glance an alphabet containing only four letters seems severely limited, but the four may be distributed on the DNA strand in virtually unlimited array. Also scientists have concluded that if the letters are grouped into three-letter words, they offer 64 word combinations. If we assume a code in which each such triplet corresponds to a letter of the English alphabet, then 5,500 bits, or nucleotides, will encode slightly more than 1,800 letters. This is enough to write a message of 360 words averaging five letters each. That, in turn, is the approximate length of the message needed to write specifications for a small bacterial virus known as ϕX174.

By the same comparison the nucleus of a single cell in the human being contains 5,000,000,000 nucleotide pairs, enough to make 1,700,000,000 letters, or 340,000,000 five-letter words. That would fill 1,000 printed volumes, 600 pages each at 500 words per page.[8] That presumably is sufficient information to build a human being, but there still must be a way to get this information into the cell factory where proteins are built.

This is where RNA (ribonucleic acid), brother to DNA, goes to work. As the DNA strands unwind, other "letters" floating freely in the cell fluid quickly attach themselves to complementary words on one of the DNA strands and form a single-threaded molecule of messenger RNA, which has a slightly different list of bases. This molecule, imprinted with the DNA message, then detaches itself and moves out of the nucleus to the cell factory. There it is picked up by a ribosome and feeds through this cell component like magnetic tape through a tape recorder. The ribosome "reads" the messenger's three-letter words, each of which names an amino acid needed to form part of a protein molecule. As each word is read, another type of RNA, called transfer RNA, selects the appropriate amino acid from the supplies in the cell fluid and carries it into place. In that way the protein molecule is built up of amino acids in the precise order called for in the original DNA message. Several protein molecules may be in the process of manufacture at once.

The indication that the genetic code is carried in triplet words made of the four bases was proved by Crick's team at Cambridge in 1961. Then Marshall Nirenberg at the National Institutes of Health in the United States worked out the specific code and won a Nobel Prize. He found one or more three-letter words, or codons, that could call up every amino acid, plus other words that act as punctuation (as in a telegram) marking the start or end of a message ordering production of a protein. Individual genes consist of variable-length "phrases" of these codons, each phrase designating a specific protein.

The process operates at great speed. DNA must copy itself each time a cell divides. A man in his reproductive lifetime may produce 500,000,000,000 sperm cells. This requires more than thirty doublings of the cell population. Thus, the information copied by the time a man has reached old age would be the equivalent of a typist copying the contents of one thousand large books thirty times in succession. George Beadle, Nobel laureate in physiology and medicine, carries the comparison to the point of paying the typist. If she charged forty-two cents per double-spaced page, it would cost fifteen million dollars. And that's only for sperm cells.[9]

For many years the gene, the basic life-form bearer, could not be visualized except as a vague, formless something, somewhere. Then the Watson-Crick DNA model indicated probable form and structure. Then another man could say: "Ah, that's what it looks like. Now let's see if I can find or make one."

The genetic dogma, therefore, is tested and modified almost daily by scientists creating microscopic realities out of theory. In 1969 a Harvard University team separated a single gene from among three thousand contained in a bacterium and photographed it. It appeared as a rope .000055 of an inch long.

The next year Dr. Gerald Weissman and Dr. Grazia Sessa at New York University created an artificial lysosome, the component in the cell now known to destroy invading agents such as virus or bacteria. Another major achievement in 1970 came from D. H. Gobind Khorana, a native of India who won the Nobel Prize in 1968. His team, then at the University of Wisconsin, created an artificial gene. It was only six months after the first man-made enzyme was revealed. Dr. Khorana has since moved to the Massachusetts Institute of Technology. At New York Dr. Weissman predicted that eventually man will learn to manufacture a human cell in its entirety. "Within twenty years," he said, "I think we will see people building entire artificial cells, or at least early models of cells to duplicate specific functions."[10]

Each time a thread is unraveled, it reveals more complex threads to be dissected, analyzed, and reconstructed. One of the most intriguing—and vital—problems is that of cell differentiation. Each cell in a human being contains *all* of the information and presumably *all* of the apparatus to make *all* of a man. Then why are cells different? How is it that one group makes a liver, another a heart, another blood, another bone, and another sperm? How do they know when to start and when to stop?

The only answer that makes sense so far is that only a small percentage of the genes in any cell are giving instructions for the operation of that particular cell. All other genes are turned off or repressed. A simple analogy on another scale would be a manufacturing plant equipped with machines to make many things, but all are covered and idle except those required to fabricate a single product. That seems an inefficient way to run a chain of factories, but who is to argue with nature, which selected this method over all others after two or three billion years of experimentation. The suppressors have been traced in some higher organisms to a special class of protein called histones, which wrap themselves around long stretches of DNA and prevent them from transferring their coded information to messenger RNA. Scientists have found some of these repressors and also have isolated enzymes believed responsible for turning the genes back on. These "inducers" work by unlocking the repressors on the segment of DNA. But from there it becomes more complicated. The repressors and inducers require enzymes of their own and probably need signals and help from other molecules, such as the recently discovered sigma, rho, and psi factors, to recognize the appropriate genes to suppress or stimulate.

One man who has tangled with details of the histone mechanism is the brilliant James Bonner at Cal Tech. Bonner combines keen insight with audaciousness and a rare ability to express his ideas lucidly. As early as 1960 he set out with Ruchih Huang, also at Cal Tech, to make a chromosome system that could synthesize RNA in a test tube. They succeeded. Then they isolated and purified the responsible enzyme—RNA polymerase—and concluded from a chain of delicate tests that the protein-histone theory is correct.

From there Bonner attempted to determine if histones are limited in number or specific for every gene. With a graduate student, Doublas Fambrough, he established that there are seven principal histones. Step by step Bonner crept experimentally toward support of his theory that the "guard dog" that determines which genes are covered by histone and which are not is a special form of RNA, which he named chromosomal RNA. Many biologists do not agree with Bonner. Some, particularly in England, still dispute that histones have anything to do with gene regulation. In fact, most of the information presented in this chapter, though representative of the best thought known, may be subject to revision by new discoveries and repudiation of old ones.

Lately it has appeared that the "Seeing Eye dog," which controls gene activity, acts in a positive rather than a negative manner. In other words, all of the genes in the DNA template may be covered until the messenger comes by and orders the histone off so that the gene can start its work. That idea intrigues Bonner because it means one could turn on certain specific genes by adding the right chromosomal RNA. Adding this RNA into a tissue culture of human cells might then allow one to switch on the manufacture of any human biochemical, such as hemoglobin in the red-blood cells. It could even provide a pathway for rebuilding tissue in the body. Bonner suggests, only half in jest, that it may one day be possible to switch on the synthesis of neurons in the brain to make up for the 100,000 we lose every day.[11]

While we wait for dependable laws to guide us, other questions proliferate. What tells liver cells when a liver is complete and when to stop making more? If part of a liver is removed, it rapidly regenerates the lost portion. What turns on the cells then? If the cells of a liver rebuild it, why not the cells of the heart or an arm or a leg? Or what keeps the "Seeing Eye dog" from going wild, permitting the uncontrolled proliferation of cells, which may be what happens in physical deformities or cancer?

The central dogma states that information can move in only one direction—from DNA to RNA to protein. However, there are indications that information also may move in the opposite direction. The cell membrane may play an important part in switching genes on and off. By feeding information back to its nucleus it may respond to environmental changes which help govern how much of what to build when. We know that when the membrane is touched by certain hormones, which serve as intercellular messengers, the membrane will respond as though jolted by an electric probe. It will send off a signal to the nucleus, triggering RNA production by genes, thus stimulating more manufacture of protein. A cell also may "know" when its class of job is done by its position within the organ. When it is no longer surrounded on all sides by others, perhaps it "knows" that the heart or liver or lung is finished and work can stop.

Bonner and his group at Cal Tech also have made some inroads into this puzzle. They set up a computer program attempting to copy the logical stages by which a single cell at the tip of a growing plant continuously divides and gives rise to a bud, a stem, tissue, and finally a flower. At each cell division, Bonner reasoned, the growing cells must test themselves for position and proximity to neighboring cells. If one finds itself all alone at the very tip of a stem, it concludes it is the apical cell and continues to divide. If it is surrounded by neighbors, then it concludes it is a bud cell, some genes are turned off, and further growth is inhibited. This "reasoning" process must somehow go on to form the epidermal cells and others which become the pithy inner structure of the stem. (At Cornell University Frederick C. Steward showed that if any one cell of a carrot plant was isolated and nurtured, it continued to act like an apical cell and grew into an entire new plant.)

Thus there are indications (shades of Lysenko) that cells somehow respond to their environment and order changes of performance to fit the circumstances. Flowering of a plant takes place when leaves of the mature plant perceive that daylight is lasting a certain length of time. When this moment occurs, they release a hormone that goes to the bud where it unlocks the flowering genes.[12]

Through the science of genetics we learned how to grow hybrid grains to yield high protein and resist disease. This kind of work led to the green revolution that is now providing the food to stave off starvation in the exploding population of the world. By selective breeding of animals we can get rid of objectionable characteristics and increase meat production.

Now, for the first time in history, we have the genetic information that may lead us to dare change the human being. We still do not know how everything is done, but when we do, the prospect for building and rebuilding men is enormous.

Gradually we are learning where specific genes for specific jobs are located on the DNA strands. Someday we may be able to stimulate a gene to do more work, such as producing insulin for diabetes victims. Someday we may be able to remove a defective gene and replace it with a good one. Someday we may be able to plant an entirely new code within an egg, building the new man to our specifications.

Among scientists these possibilities are not maybes but virtual certainties. "The living organisms of today have had the benefit of two billion years of selective molecular evolution," stated Robert L. Sinsheimer, head of biology at Cal Tech. "Soon we shall have that cumulative ingenuity at our fingertips . . . and with it not only the power to alter the natural world but to alter our very selves."[13]

We are very near to mastery of the most vital techniques in the history of man and just as near to crucial decisions which may alter his path for all time. In the words of Alexander Pope:

> Know then thyself, presume not God to scan.
> The proper study of mankind is man.
> Placed on this isthmus of a middle state,
> A being darkly wise and rudely great.

CHAPTER 9

Genetic
Mistakes

In 1716 a child named Edward Lambert was born in England. His parents were normal, and Edward himself was not unusual at birth. A few months later his skin began to turn yellow. Then it became black and grew rough and scaly with projecting inch-long bristles.

No one knows the tortures he suffered as a child, growing up with such a gross abnormality, but they called Edward the porcupine man. He was widely exhibited as a circus freak.

Despite the intricate pathways we have found to the core of life, no scientist has yet attempted to define the special chemistry by which a man and woman are drawn together, in beauty or ugliness, to ensure continuation of the species. Each must find his own magic, and so Edward found a wife.

He fathered a son, who inherited the gross black porcupine growth over his body. Then there were two more sons and two daughters, all of whom apparently suffered the same disease, though it is not known for certain.

Medical accounts followed the first son. He, too, found a wife, who gave birth to six sons and a daughter. Two and possibly three of the boys likewise were porcupine men. Uncertain records indicate the affliction reached one more boy in the following generation. He would have been the great-grandson of the original, but there the porcupine syndrome vanished, perhaps forever.[1]

These mutants, occurring in four generations of one family, were victims of what is considered the rarest genetic disease in medical history. The molecular accident which caused it is not known, but it demonstrates that the genes are not infallible. In the trillions of times they copy themselves to make new cells they may be damaged or altered by countless things, including nuclear radiation. It is this fact—that genes are *not unchangeable*—that makes the entire range of evolution possible. If early genes had "crystallized" or armored themselves somehow against outside forces, evolution would have stopped sometime in the past. Plants and animals would have been unable to adapt to changing conditions, and today's intelligent ape would not have appeared. So we should never forget that although the code by which information is retransmitted appears to be universal, phrases in the code may change or mutate. Some such changes are good, leading to a higher order, but most are not and lead to errors of malformation and disease.

Our genes are located within twenty-three *pairs* of chromosomes, of which only one pair carries sexual traits to the next generation. The other twenty-two are called autosomal chromosomes. The porcupine man was an example of autosomal disease, as is the well-known sickle-cell mutant gene. This gene, common among Negroid people of tropical origin (though that origin may have been many generations ago), produces red blood cells shaped like a sickle rather than the flat, round normal shape. The result is severe and often fatal anemia, but also more complicated than that. The sickle cell may cause a condition known as tower skull resulting from overactivity of bone marrow in producing replacement cells. Side effects include weakness and lassitude, impaired mental function, poor physical development, heart failure, paralysis from brain damage, rheumatism, pneumonia, abdominal pain and kidney failure from reduced oxygen, and enlargement and fibrosis of the spleen as a result of the collection of many damaged red blood cells. At a glance it would seem obvious that one tiny genetic mistake is responsible for many ills of black people. Conversely, if this defect could be remedied, it would yield great social as well as health rewards.

How and why would nature have tossed such a harmful gene into the stream of evolution? The difference between sickle-cell and normal blood is the replacement of a single molecule, and it turns out not to have been a mistake at all. Where this mutation arose, it is advantageous. People with sickle-cell blood are resistant to malaria; those with normal blood are not. So evolution was wise in placing this gene mutation in malaria-infested parts of the world where it would help to continue development of human life, but it was unable to foresee that Africans would move elsewhere and develop anemia and its associated ills.

Genetic abnormality, while accounting for gross deformities and such conditions as albinoism, also causes an ever-growing list of human ailments. More than nine hundred such disorders have so far been classified. Four were known as early as 1908, but most of the list has been compiled only within the past twenty years. Some are more serious than others and become more significant for two main reasons. First, as other diseases are brought under control, these become more prominent. Second, genetic abnormalities are increasing because elements in our environment are creating more mutations. Such elements include exposure to radiation from use of X rays for medical diagnosis and treatment and nuclear radiation from atomic weapons tests and power production. A particle of radiation entering or passing through the body may damage or alter a cell's genes and chromosomes. Many foods, cosmetic items, and chemicals may do the same, including coffee and cigarette smoke.

About one person in twenty or twenty-five is born with a significant genetic defect. That means three to four million of the eighty million babies born each year in the world. Of these perhaps one million carry defects *not* linked with sex chromosomes. About 5 percent result from sex-linked mutant genes. Another one million or more may carry gross chromosome mistakes. A third one million suffer developmental abnormalities not fully understood. These figures, estimated by the United Nations Scientific Committee on Effects of Atomic Radiation, do not include possibly one million more abortions, stillbirths, and children who die within a month after birth from genetic flaws.[2]

Each chromosome carries thousands of genes, but only one chromosome pair out of the twenty-three is responsible for sexual characteristics of the new person. Women have two identical sex-determining chromosomes, known as XX, one of which is contributed to a new being. To match this, the male also has an X chromosome, but also a shorter stubbier variety called the Y chromosome. Thus in an egg fertilization the woman is sure to contribute an X, but the man may contribute an X or a Y. If the female X joins the male Y, the result is a son. If both contribute an X, the result is a daughter. As we shall see, it is possible to obtain abnormal combinations of these special chromosomes, but genes within an otherwise normal pair also may contribute genetic faults and disease.[3]

In human embryos the beginning of the sex organs, or gonads, is first seen at about five weeks of gestation time, when a pair of ridges begins to grow out from the embryonic kidney. For a while the gonads develop in an identical fashion in both sexes, composed of the same components. Apparently if a Y chromosome is present, the gonads become testes. If it is not present, the gonads become ovaries. Factors that influence maleness or femaleness, according to some geneticists, still depend upon little-understood environmental factors in the womb. Thus it is that even though the chromosomes have cast their vote toward male or female, many people are born with a varying mixture of male and female characteristics.[4]

Many gene defects are lethal. In fact, every person carries from two to four different recessive genes, which would prevent a child from being born alive. Such genes are responsible for many miscarriages and natural abortions, nature's way of eliminating misfits from the population. Recessive traits do not kill unless the same one is passed to the child by both parents. Since most married couples begin as strangers, the chance of this happening is relatively slight. Marrying a near relative, however, greatly increases the chance of sex-related genes passing to the child, leading to both chronic and fatal diseases.

The classic example of a congenital disorder caused by a sex-linked recessive gene is hemophilia, a defect in the blood-clotting mechanism. Known as bleeders, hemophiliacs often die in childhood because any minor cut is a threat to life. Uncontrolled internal bleeding also may occur from heavy exercise or a bruise. It occurs almost exclusively in men, though women may be carriers of the bad gene. Hemophilia is often referred to as the royal disease because of famous cases that brought it prominently to medical attention. The first known royal carrier of the gene was Queen Victoria of England, who married her cousin, Prince Albert.

On April 7, 1853, the queen gave birth to the eighth of her nine children, Leopold, who was sickly from infancy. It soon became evident that he bled profusely from trivial injuries. When he was fifteen, it was reported that "His Royal Highness has been suffering during the last week from severe accidental hemorrhage. The Prince was reduced to a state of extreme and dangerous exhaustion by the loss of blood, but has since greatly recovered." Of Victoria's nine children, one son became a victim of the disease, and two, possibly three, daughters were carriers, transmitting the gene to succeeding generations of Europe's intermixed royal families.

The sex-linked recessive defect originally results from the mutation of a gene in the X chromosome of a germ cell—from either the sperm of the father or the egg of the mother. If the child is a male, he will be hemophiliac; if a female, she will rarely suffer from the disease, but she will be a carrier of it. The chances are one out of two that her sons will be hemophiliac and her daughters carriers. The sons of a hemophiliac father will carry no trace of the defect, since they receive his Y (and not his X) chromosome. All his daughters, however, will be carriers.[5]

One form of muscular dystrophy is inherited as a sex-linked trait. Absence of teeth, as in the "toothless men of Sind," color blindness, and a form of night blindness are also sex-linked traits. One type of rickets may result from a dominant sex gene. One peculiar genetic flaw causes a deficiency of one enzyme in red blood cells. Persons with this defect often do not know it, but if they are treated with the antimalarial drug primequine or certain sulfonamides, they suffer acute anemia. If the offending substances are removed, they recover.

Although the conditions mentioned arise from genes that mutated or were miscopied, gross abnormalities also result from chromosomes that are duplicated, mislocated, or inverted. This can happen either in plants or in animals.

One dreaded quirk is the mongoloid idiot, a child born with misshapen head and body, retarded in physical and mental development. These children rarely live long, but a few reach maturity and reproduce. In 1959 it was found in France that this abnormality results from the presence of an extra whole chromosome in the victim's cells. The chance of giving birth to a mongoloid child increases with the age of the mother. The odds range from about fifteen per ten thousand births in young mothers to several cases per one hundred in women near the end of their reproductive years. The extra chromosome is believed to be contributed through the female egg resulting from the irregular distribution of one particular pair of chromosomes during the four-way division (meiosis) when the germ cells are formed.

Science has found a way to detect the likelihood of the

occurrence of mongolism. The examination can be performed by taking a blood sample or other cells from the mother. This is one of several ways in which modern research offers hope for reducing abnormalities in future generations.

The word "abnormality" is a pallid clinical term which in no way describes the personal misery and mental anguish suffered by the family where a major accident of nature occurs. Each time a parent looks at his misshapen child he blames himself for bringing this affliction into the world and then will spend his energy and resources trying to repair or cope with it. It is small consolation to realize that a genetic flaw is not the personal fault of parents and that thousands of other people suffer the same agonies.

Several examples of lifelong suffering come from defects in the combination of sex chromosomes. One is called Turner's disease, in which the victim receives only one X instead of the normal XX (female) or XY(male). Such a person looks like a woman but is sterile because the ovaries are either incomplete or missing. Klinefelder's syndrome consists of two X chromosomes plus a Y (XXY). The result is a man who is sterile with underdeveloped testicles. An XXX abnormality is also known. This produces a woman with underdeveloped sexual organs, body contour, and hair distribution.[6]

The single Y chromosome, which seems to fight three-to-one odds in the uterine struggle to produce a man, has aroused public attention because some men are born with forty-seven (instead of the normal forty-six) chromosomes, receiving an extra Y (XYY). There are indications this extra dose of Y chromosome intensifies male aggression and may lead to criminal tendencies. First knowledge of this came from surveys of tall men in institutions for the criminally insane, many of whom were aggressive and antisocial. Cal Tech scientists calculated that the XYY syndrome is found most often among men who are tall and criminal, tall and criminally insane, criminally insane without regard to height, tall and mentally ill, or tall and mentally retarded.

The technique for chromosomal determination involves microscopic examination of blood cells sampled from inside the cheeks.[7] In order to gain a better statistical base for understanding the XYY syndrome, Dr. Lawrence Razavi, a Stanford University geneticist, tested eighty-three men who had been imprisoned for various crimes. Fourteen percent revealed abnormal sex chromosomes, which is twenty-five to thirty times the proportion of such irregularities in the general male population.

"What we seem to have," Dr. Razavi said, "is a small but important group of people whose biological oddness makes them especially vulnerable to social pressures that most people can handle easily. Sex crime seems to be one result of this oddness. There may be others."[8]

He warned against drawing hasty generalizations from meager data because other factors may be at work. A study of female criminals indicated that certain hormones, or their temporary lack, may play a role in crime. This survey of 249 women prisoners revealed that 62 percent of their crimes were committed during the week preceding their menstrual periods.[9]

Judicious use of hormones *can* produce short-term changes in human behavior, such as the female hormone estrogen which inhibits aggressive behavior in men, but the XYY chromosome question is more fundamental. If it can be verified that this flaw leads to hyperaggression and crime, the social results in crime prevention could be enormous. As part of standard physical examinations, all young boys could be screened for the XYY flaw before adolescence, when aggressive tendencies begin to be socially troublesome.

A broad pilot study of this sort was undertaken in 1970 by Dr. Digamber Borgaonkar, of Johns Hopkins University, under a grant from the National Institute of Mental Health. He began taking blood samples from 6,400 youths, age eight to eighteen, in Maryland juvenile institutions, comparing these with an equal number of youngsters in the general population.

The study was halted because he was accused of drawing his control group from poverty areas and minority groups.[10]

That reaction calls to mind society's instinct for intolerance and pecking the weakest or misshapen members to death. When it becomes possible to screen all young boys for the XYY factor, there is danger this tiny minority would be labeled potential criminals and wear a badge of shame and suspicion all their lives. In a rational world, on the other hand, these boys would be singled out for special education and training to turn their extra dose of aggression into channels of social value. In years ahead newfound knowledge concerning genetic predisposition to crime may be put to use in altering behavior so that such individuals may become productive members of society rather than criminal detriments.

Methods of achieving behavior control, however, may be unacceptably severe in light of current beliefs and morality. A case in point is a middle-aged Denver man who was castrated at his own request in 1972 after his admission in court that in his adult lifetime he had molested from four hundred to five hundred girls under twelve years of age. According to District Judge Robert E. McLean, the operation at Denver General Hospital was permitted only after the man insisted upon it as his only hope for cure. After the operation the man said he was cured. He was described as more docile, less aggressive, and more humble.

Sex-linked aberrations are perhaps more sensational, but many other diseases and defects result from the other twenty-two chromosome pairs. A common one is sugar diabetes. Predisposition to this disease is inherited by five out of every one hundred persons, although only about 20 percent of those develop obvious symptoms. Goitrous cretinism results from defects in iodine metabolism, and one form is inherited.

Other chromosome flaws involve damage to the central nervous system. Phenylketonuria is severe mental deficiency caused by failure to oxidize a certain acid. Amaurotic idiocy is a recessive strain that causes fat to accumulate in the brain. It results in early death. Another anomaly is Wilson's disease, nervous-system damage resulting from lack of an essential copper-containing protein. Huntington's chorea, also inherited, brings degeneration of the nervous system and death. It usually occurs between ages forty and forty-five, which means that by the time a man knows he has the disease, he has already passed it on to half of his children.[11]

The genes and chromosomes form a marvelous system for transmitting information from one generation to the next, but it is a fallible system which creates a chamber of horrors of genetic mutations, the potential failure implicit in the very end which nature left open for evolutionary progress. This open end was designed to permit organisms to adapt to changing environment, but the list of genetic defects grows longer. Some scientists believe the human being inherits a predisposition to *all* of the physical and mental ills which beset him in a lifetime. We think of moving toward superman out of man, but we may find evolution can move down as well as up.

There are indications that the number of harmful genetic mutations in the total world population is increasing rather than decreasing. If left to our natural state, we could expect severe genetic faults to disappear by natural selection. The faulty child would die before he could pass the flaw on to another generation. This happens, of course, but the laws of probability show that almost as fast as such defects are removed, they appear again through recurrent mutations somewhere else. Some may reappear by chance—such as Huntington's chorea, which occurs once in a million eggs or sperm cells—or through natural mutating forces such as cosmic rays or radiation from ores in the earth.

Now, however, we must add to that statistical base the genetic changes we are inflicting upon ourselves in the modern drug-chemical-industrial civilization. One important source is X ray, an important tool in diagnostic medicine. Also our atmosphere and the earth contain residual man-made radiation particles from atomic weapons tests and production of nuclear power. Growing awareness of genetic danger is why special care is taken not to irradiate human reproductive organs or the unborn fetus.

But what about things that change genes and chromosomes elsewhere in our bodies? We depend upon accurate transmission of information when cells divide to restore those lost in normal wear and tear of our vital organs. Any one of a thousand chemical substances, taken at the wrong time or in wrong quantity, may cause genetic damage. They are called mutagens. Yet we accept a world in which our air and water are polluted with gases and chemicals.

A cigarette-smoker inhales alien material which may damage and mutate lung cells. We take drugs to cure disease or sleeplessness or fatigue, but no one knows the genetic changes that may result from chronic use or accumulation of these materials. Scientists estimate that a person who drinks two cups of coffee every morning does more genetic damage than if he lived within the boundary of a nuclear power plant.

Alcohol is a serious offender. In 1971 Dr. Denes de Torok, a biologist at Carnegie-Mellon University, tested three groups of one hundred people. The first contained patients committed to Mayview Mental Hospital near Pittsburgh with permanent brain damage caused by alcoholism. The second one hundred were Mayview outpatients, also alcoholics but not yet brain-damaged sufficiently to require hospitalization. The third group consisted of students and faculty from the university, none of whom were alcoholics, although some were social drinkers.

Dr. de Torok told the National Council on Alcoholism that *all* of the first group revealed genetic damage. Beyond that, he found damaged chromosomes in more than half of all the cells he examined, indicating that most all of the body cells were affected. The second one hundred, alcoholic outpatients, included ninety-five with some chromosomes damaged. The third group of students and faculty appeared to be normal. There is the slim possibility that damaged chromosomes might have been the original *cause* of alcoholism, but De Torok believes the opposite—that excessive drinking leads to general chromosome damage. The alcoholic not only harms himself but also may transmit damaged chromosomes in germ cells. "If this genetic damage occurs in a person's reproductive stage of life," Dr. de Torok said, "he could contribute only damaged material to offspring."[12]

The same could be true of drug abuse, which has ensnared millions of young people in the current generation. Evidence is still inadequate to judge the degree of harm in marijuana-smoking or the genetic damage caused by taking amphetamines, barbiturates, or even heroin. There is specific danger, though, in the hallucinogenic drugs, including LSD and mescaline.

Studies have indicated that LSD in particular may alter the germ cells, passing defects to new generations of babies. The extent of this danger has not been clearly established, but it adds new reason for concern over spreading drug addiction, which already threatens the nation with crime and crowded mental institutions. The danger is compounded by the fact that youthful drug abuse is frequently linked with sexual promiscuity. This means that more genetic defects are "infecting" a growing number of illegitimate babies. How these will multiply in coming generations can only be conjectured. We know the nation suffers some six million alcoholics. If there are that many drug abusers in the twelve-to-thirty-year-old population, then millions of chromosomal aberrations of varying severity may be expected.

There is one more major factor leading to an increase of genetic illness. This, paradoxically, is the fault of the medical profession itself, as we learn better techniques for treating human illness and abnormalities. Sugar diabetes is controlled by administering insulin. Defective hearts are mended. A faulty valve, resulting from misinformation in the genes, may be replaced with an artificial one. Thalidomide babies are equipped with prosthetic arms and legs so they may lead seminormal lives. Many mental illnesses can now be treated symptomatically, and mongoloids are carefully nursed to keep them alive.

We cannot fault the medical profession for doing everything possible to heal people. Compassion for the defective is the highest mark of an enlightened civilization. But soon we must ask: Which is the greater good—saving the individual or saving generations yet unborn? In primitive societies deformed babies were allowed to die. We keep them alive, and they marry and have their own children. As stated by Dr. Donald R. Scoby, professor of botany at North Dakota State University: "The technology advancing the area of medical death control has resulted in the genetic makeup of men being polluted with 'bad' genes. The result, such as some mental illness and open spine, can be treated in the present generations, but when passed on through heredity without natural control, contaminate the genetic makeup of man. Thus man as a species will be weakened."[13]

This point was reinforced by Dr. Bentley Glass, distinguished professor at the State University of New York in Stony Brook:

> We must recognize that under our present application of ethics to medical practice, human society is already doing itself a considerable eugenic injury. When an infant or child with a genetic defect is kept alive by medical means and its defect is controlled or eliminated, the child grows to adulthood. The most common sequel is marriage and parenthood.
>
> In the past, under a more cruel rule of nature, such persons never lived to reproduce, and their defective genes were eliminated from the population. The population thus maintained a balance between the defective genes being eliminated in each generation and new ones being produced through mutation.
>
> Not all mutations produce defective genes, but over ninety-nine percent of them do so for the simple reason that the genes we now have are the product of millions of years of selection of the best. Medical practices thus tend to increase the frequency of defective genes in the population. To a certain ex-

tent, doctors are only making more work for themselves, for since they have not removed the cause of the defect, the gene, they have only corrected the symptoms. The defective gene, when transmitted, does the same harm once again.[14]

This warning by Dr. Glass was spoken in 1967, yet only now are we beginning to heed it, and only upon a fragmentary scale, which must be expanded a thousandfold if we expect to slow or reverse the flood of "bad" genes into our future society.

It is strange, but perhaps prophetic, that we are becoming aware of the danger of spreading genetic disease at a time when we are already worried about overpopulation. That worry usually centers upon the more tangible threats of malnutrition, starvation, overcrowding, and planetary pollution which in themselves are leading toward degeneration of the human race. So the two worries are closely linked. For the future of society and the growth of man, the only danger worse than an exploding population is a population exploding with people already defective from inheritance.

Strong forces are at work on the population problem. Parents are urged to have smaller families. The birth-control pill, though it carries some genetic dangers within itself, is helping young couples have fewer children. Since World War II Japan has curbed its population growth through birth control and abortion. In India men are paid to undergo sterilization, and in the United States an increasing number of states are relaxing abortion laws.

Disregarding the moral arguments involved, if we are bent upon reducing the number of people in the world, why not do it selectively to reduce *defective* people rather than just a gross reduction in numbers? For many years scientists have been applying crossbreeding techniques to eliminate bad traits and increase the good in grains, fruits, and food animals. Many of these techniques could be applied directly to human beings. Isn't it time we put them to work?

That question poses a serious dilemma. It involves the fundamental question of free will—the individual's freedom to select a mate and have children according to his desire. If an idiot marries an idiot, no one can legally challenge their right to breed more idiots. The thought of exercising even the slightest control over human breeding smacks of the world of "1984," with government controlling all human freedoms. In the past decade, however, we have been subjected to an intense barrage of propaganda, verging upon coercion, to reduce the population. It is only one step farther, and probably a good one, to coax people even more urgently *not* to have children if there is a probability of transmitting genetic flaws. This is supported by the fact that most parents, if they knew they carried defective genes, would not wish to pass these defects to their children. It is not pleasant rearing a deformed or mentally retarded child. The way to start reducing the faulty genes in our society is to prevent these children from being born, and it can begin without government intervention.

Until recent years parents had no way of knowing they carried eugenic disease until a defective child was born. Then it was too late. Now there is a growing specialty of genetic counseling by which couples may obtain expert advice on the odds of producing defective children. Such advice enables them to decide whether or not to have a child, or even whether or not to get married. The latter decision might be made if both potential partners carry ancestral traits that together magnify the chance of transmitting deformity. As Dr. Scoby stated:

> The first step toward accomplishing man's survival lies in the development and acceptance of a thorough genetic counseling system, its success necessarily aided by legalized abortion. Through these steps man eventually would be able to eliminate the birth of individuals with inherited defects, and the genetic pool of man would be strengthened.
>
> We do not question that we as humans care enough about life to care for those whose lives are nearly useless to themselves and others, but would it not be better to stop bringing these lives into the world? Who suffers more from our supposed kindness than the disabled individuals? A far more generous and realistic approach would be to eliminate the birth of the

defected rather than encouraging the nursing of those unfit for a productive and satisfying life.[15]

The change in American attitudes toward sex and reproduction in the past ten years has been revolutionary. A decade ago it would have been a foolhardy man who dared to speak this way on matters of abortion and "elimination" of defective babies. America has been the heartland of puritanical and hypocritical sex mores. The nation's growth was built upon the honor and righteousness of large families. If such a family occasionally contained a malformed or retarded youngster, that child was regarded as a special charge, a cross to be borne with patience and fortitude. The early American family took care of its own mistakes.

Then the family began to dissolve. Divorce became commonplace. Children from broken homes were less cared for, and the deformed ones were shuffled off to state and county institutions to live or die in lonely solitude. Such factors led to a progressive dissolution of ethics and morals, but paradoxically they also carried the seeds of a new shape for humanity. We now see uncontrolled population growth as a disease that could destroy the world. The pill and easy sterilization provide almost certain methods to prevent conception, and the revolution in biology shows us the threat of genetic degeneration.

So genetic counseling is the first step in man's remaking his own revolutionary future. It began some years ago when the only tools available were the mathematical rules formed by Mendel, the Austrian monk. Most people still do not know they might carry a recessive gene endangering their offspring. Others wonder anxiously. Such couples may be referred to a genetic specialist by a family doctor. Through interviews the geneticist can determine if parents or grandparents of a young couple were sufferers of a disease such as diabetes. If the same traits show up in the ancestry of both marriage partners, he can advise that their children are likely to inherit.

Medical columnist Dr. Walter Alvarez points out that 250,000 defective children are born in the United States each year and that in many cases a geneticist could have warned the parents ahead of time. A woman who knows that a parent or grandparent suffered from hemophilia, for example, should make sure that her intended husband is free of the taint. If both were carriers, it is probable that four out of four children would be afflicted.[16]

Today the genetic advisor has precise new tools to work with. Now a simple blood sample can reveal a map of the chromosomes, known as a karyotype. (This is the technique used in the study of prison inmates to estimate the XYY factor in criminal behavior.) The karyotype can show a young married couple positively whether or not they carry inheritable chromosome damage. Biologists each year are refining the technique to identify specific diseases which may be passed on to children. According to Dr. James V. Neel, of the University of Michigan, doctors can now recognize more than fifty genetic diseases in the carrier state by chromosome study.

The near miracles which can be performed with this knowledge may be illustrated by a rare genetic disease and a baby girl who inherited it. The malady is Tay-Sachs disease, a pernicious and fatal condition which primarily attacks Jewish children. Born with this gene defect, a child cannot manufacture a particular enzyme that the body needs to break down certain fats in the nerve cells. The fats eventually accumulate, burst the nerve cells, and destroy the nervous system.

One little girl who suffered this disease was born, apparently healthy, to a young couple living in a Philadelphia suburb. Shortly after she was four months old, she began to fail, and doctors informed the parents there was little chance she would live. They reconciled themselves to her death, but they wanted another child, although fearing it would suffer the same fate. By chromosome study doctors assured them that another child would be unlikely to have the defect. So they attempted another pregnancy.

At this point medical researchers were able to employ an even newer medical technique called amniocentesis. *Amnio* refers to the amniotic fluid that surrounds a fetus in the womb. *Centesis* refers to the use of a long hollow needle, like a large hypodermic syringe. A doctor inserts the needle through the mother's abdominal wall and into the uterine sac to withdraw some of the amniotic fluid. The procedure, though not yet common, is little more painful than a pin prick. It does not harm the fetus or cause infection if carefully done.

The unborn baby swims in this fluid, swallows it, and eliminates waste in it. Some cells of the fetus are contained in it, thus many diagnoses may be made from the amniotic fluid, which may be sampled as early as the twelfth week of pregnancy. An interesting result is that the fluid can tell positively if the baby is a boy or a girl, but determining sex to satisfy parental curiosity is less important than its role in predicting the likelihood of certain diseases. Tay-Sachs is one of them.

Under the care of Dr. Sheldon H. Cherry, a New York obstetrician and a pioneer in amniocentesis, the Philadelphia mother who had lost a daughter was assured, during her pregnancy, that her next child would not suffer the defect. She gave birth to a healthy son.[17]

At the University of Chicago a team headed by Dr. Reuben Matalon and Dr. Albert Dorfman developed a direct chemical analysis for the amniotic fluid, reducing the time previously needed for growth of cell cultures and chromosome examination. The technique analyzes a group of chemical compounds called mucopolysaccharides. If these exist in abnormal amounts or form, it signals the presence of genetic flaws.

"The new procedure is faster, cheaper, and more accurate," said Dr. Dorfman. "This means prospective parents can terminate a pregnancy, if they so decide, without undue risk to the mother. In the past all such a couple could do was either take their chances with the probability factors or refrain from having children. Such couples now can get a definitive diagnosis of normalcy while they still have the option of ending the pregnancy. This enables them to avoid bearing deformed children and to have as many normal children as they choose."[18]

Prevention is far preferable to a cure in virtually all cases, but scientists are now making progress toward the difficult goal of repairing genetic flaws *after* a child is born with them. This involves either replacing a bad gene on the chromosome strands or implanting a good gene where one is absent. The prospect of performing transplant surgery within the submicroscopic nucleus of a human cell and then repeating it millions or billions of times is so remote as to appear impossible. Scientific ingenuity, however, is prospecting with ways to trick viruses into doing this infinitely complex job. The theory is basically simple. Since viruses invade the cell and implant their own code upon the chromosomes, why not have them carry beneficial genes into place?

The first successful experiment in this direction was reported in 1971 by three molecular biologists: Carl Merril, Mark Geier, and John Petricciani at the National Institutes of Health in Bethesda, Maryland. They began by taking cells from a victim of the hereditary disease called galactosemia. Because of a gene defect, the patient was unable to produce the essential enzyme that enables the body to metabolize galactose, a simple sugar found in milk. Unless an infant born with this defect is quickly placed on a milk-free diet, he faces malnutrition, mental retardation, and eventual death.

To correct the flaw, the scientists chose a bacteriophage (a virus that preys on bacteria) containing a gene which orders manufacture of the missing enzyme. Once the proper virus was found, the challenge was to see if they could induce it to enter the cells taken from the galactosemia patient. They incubated a mixture of virus and cells in a laboratory flask and then tested to determine if the virus had actually invaded the cells with the beneficial gene. By a series of subtle tests they found that the genetic transplant had indeed taken place, in millions of cells at once. It soon became apparent that the new hybrid cells were reproducing themselves according to the pattern containing the proper gene to correct the defect. This offers the prospect that an extract prepared in this manner could be injected into a patient with genetic disease, inducing all the body cells to take up the new correct pattern. Experiments with laboratory animals are now under way.[19]

Although many advanced techniques such as this are not quite ready for human application, ways are forming to begin the long, tedious process of cleansing deformed genes and chromosomes out of the world's bloodstream. Whether this can proceed faster than new defects are introduced depends partially upon how soon genetic counseling, preventive diagnosis, and genetic transplants become standard medical practice.

This should happen quickly. As legal sanction of therapeutic abortion spreads from state to state, more and more parents will be able to make the decision not to bring malformed children into life. Also, as the world becomes more aware of the scope of genetic dangers, it is possible that lawmakers may eventually require a karyotype chromosome map as a prerequisite to marriage, just as most states now require tests for venereal disease. Eventually one could visualize a world in which a chromosome map is made of everyone at an early age and the information carried on a wallet card or dog tag just as blood-type information is carried by every soldier and sailor. Then, if a boy and girl met and liked each other, they could compare cards to see if their union is likely to produce defective offspring. This might help them decide not to marry, but since that interferes with the mysterious and immutable laws of love, it would at least forewarn them of the genetic dangers of producing offspring.

In any case, these tools will allow individuals a free choice which could help change the world for the better. It is wonderful to imagine thousands of hospital beds and mental wards gradually emptied of their pitiful burden of misshapen people who suffered only from being born to the wrong parents. The benefits to society would be incalculable, both in mental anguish not suffered and in physical resources saved, which are now sadly wasted in the attempt to maintain life and a semblance of health in malformed people. Lifting the burden of genetic defectives could release a large fraction of human energy to more creative pursuits. As we learn to control our population, we could also build better men and women.

Beyond karyotyping, and with techniques for genetic surgery, new road maps are being drawn into the workings of the human cell. We may even discover order in the special chaos that occurs when cells run wild in the terrible family of diseases called cancer.

CHAPTER 10

Cancer

We marvel at the miracle of beginning when egg meets sperm. Chromosomal strands of mother and father twine about one another to set the shape of a new creature. The cell divides, again and again, at dazzling speed. At first the genes seem to be practicing finger exercises from eternity's piano lessons, repeating ancient proteins from the dawn of evolution. Then they play more elaborate forms in concert. Cells become aware that they are to be liver or spleen or heart. They divide and build according to the plan laid down in the chromosomes, repeating precisely as they are told, even to the mutational defect that may have been transmitted by parent cells.

A child is born in beauty, and an anxious father peers through the window of a hospital nursery, counting fingers and toes. It is all there. Nature, the master pattern-maker, has done it again.

The child grows. It becomes a strapping young man of rippling muscles or a beautiful young woman who ripples more subtly within fat-gentled curves.

Then one day—and the time is no special time—something

happens. It may be an itchy wart, but more likely it occurs deep inside, where organs and viscera slip softly around each other on mucus velvet, or in the stomach, where acids digest food, or in the pink sponge of lung tissue, where blood takes on its cargo of oxygen. One day there is a strange lump, a cough, or a stab of pain. Then we know something has gone wrong. The cells, which we did not feel or hear in their busy manufacture of new tissue, are no longer following the original design in the genes and chromosomes. From somewhere, somehow, they have received new orders from an alien master bent upon revolution. The cells, not unlike people, follow the new direction slavishly as they followed the old. No longer constrained by the status quo of making liver or muscle or bone, they multiply wildly in alien forms. Violent new growth takes shape, deformed cells dividing with riotous speed, multiplying and devouring the old society from which they came.

This is cancer.

The word invokes a peculiar dread above all other diseases. It may strike any person at any age in any part of the body, then lead to physical decay and protracted suffering. Until recent years cancer was virtually synonymous with death. Even now the possibility of surviving many forms of it is slight or nonexistent, though tremendous advances have been made in methods of treatment. It creeps into a vital organ when least expected and often has progressed beyond the curative power of medical skill before its presence is known.

More than 300,000 Americans die of cancer each year. As a cause of death it ranks number two behind heart and circulation disorders. It is the number-one killer of children up to age fifteen. Overall, cancer is increasing despite an advancing wave of national and international research seeking early detection, prevention, and cure. Lung cancer alone caused 60,000 deaths in 1970, compared with 3,000 in 1915.[1]

These facts and fears we already know, but within this century we may come to know enough more to throw final barricades around this putrifying killer as we learned through the past century to control the source of many bacterial and viral infections. Curing or preventing cancer, however, has proved to be a task more formidable than discovering a smallpox vaccine.

Cancer is not an *it*, but a multitude of maladies. More than one hundred different forms have been identified. Each is unique. Each presents a different rate of growth, danger of recurrence, and ability to spread. Each offers its own specific challenge to the surgical, chemical, and radiation weapons marshaled against its ravaging invasion. Physicians are confronted by a multifaceted monster which, wherever it appears, usurps the machinery of normal growth and destroys the organism in which it flourishes.

Hopefully this monster will reveal itself eventually in a common source or cause which will permit counterattack at the origin, but at the moment we know one thing for certain: *Cancer is life gone wild.* It works its death within the cell, using the genes and chromosomes which normally labor devotedly through a lifetime to maintain the pattern set by ancestry to create and sustain a plant or an animal or a man. How it invades and utilizes the core mechanism of life is the mystery. When we lift the seventh veil to that complexity, then we may launch the final attack against cancer. Until then we fight a delaying action.

The three primary weapons are surgery to remove the tumor, radiation to kill the wild growth of cells, and chemical therapy to block or slow their growth. When these are used alone or in combination, coupled with early detection, there is good hope for extending a cancer patient's life. In some cases the cancer is cured. A "cure" is generally defined as survival for five or more years without recurrence.

Malignant growths have been recognized for a thousand years. Cancer surgery has been practiced at least half that long, though success was meager before the twentieth century. A benign tumor is one that is self-contained and lends itself to removal. Malignancy, which spreads uncontrollably, is another matter. Surgery is difficult because a few malignant cells may be left behind to spread again in healthy tissue.

Another problem with many cancers is the tendency to spread from a central source to other parts of the body in a process known as metastasis. It is difficult to detect the tendrils or cell colonies creeping out to new organs until a surgical incision is made. This exploration often reveals only that it is too late.

In some advanced cases radiation therapy slows the malignancy. Sometimes it reduces the growth, giving the patient a few more years to live. Radiation was first applied to cancer shortly after Röntgen discovered X rays and was used against leukemia—cancer of the blood—as early as 1902. Following discovery of radium by Marie and Pierre Curie in 1898, radium therapy also was attempted. In the same period researchers recognized that radiation, while killing cancer cells, also damaged the surrounding tissues, particularly the germ cells. An early protective measure was the use of lead shielding to guard X-ray machine operators against sterility.

Because of the difficulty of concentrating radiation within a malignancy without destroying healthy tissue, this therapy has remained only a partial success, though the technology has improved through the years. In 1940 the betatron entered the arena. This is a particle accelerator that generates electrons more powerful than X ray. It was applied selectively to cancer during World War II while the atomic bomb was being developed. The bomb killed thousands and condemned more to malignant death in later years, but it also opened the door to nuclear fission and a ready supply of radioactive isotopes which have blessed mankind with new tools for diagnosis and treatment.

In 1951 cobalt 60, a radioactive isotope now produced in quantity by nuclear reactors, was introduced to cancer therapy. This concentrated source of powerful radiation made it possible to treat cancer patients more selectively. With radiation focused to a narrow point, the patient was rotated under the beam so that the energy could be concentrated within the tumor without prolonged exposure of a single area of healthy tissue.[2]

In the 1960's high-voltage radiation therapy was expanded to a number of different cancers. Some patients suffering Hodgkin's disease, cancer in the lymphatic system, were exposed to radiation from a six-million-volt linear accelerator. With mild treatment seven out of nine patients lived two years without recurrence. With heavier treatment seven out of fifteen patients remained free of cancer after five years.

Victims of advanced lung cancer normally do not live more than six months, but some may now enjoy a few more years of life through super-voltage radiotherapy. In one test all of eighty-two patients so treated responded well. Forty-eight survived a year, twenty-four lived two years, and six were still active after five years.[3]

Literally thousands of drugs have been tried against cancer, many brewed by charlatans who offered powerless potions to gullible victims desperate for any remedy. Even today it is not unusual to hear of a miracle drug or chemical touted as a cancer cure. Despite the best advice of legitimate medical practitioners, many people succumb to such quackery when other avenues of cure have been exhausted. The dubious efficacy of some magic drug is further confused by the fact that some malignancies, after confounding all treatment, may reverse course and cure themselves. No panacea exists for cancer, but its unpredictable nature makes it impossible to ignore any hopeful possibility.

Some forms of malignancy have been treated successfully by chemicals in recent years, often in combination with surgery and radiation. Chemotherapy includes substances ranging from synthetic drugs to natural extracts from the body. For example, in 1949 diethylstilbestrol, a synthetic hormone, was first used in treating cancer of the prostate.

During the past twenty years scientists have analyzed thousands of drugs and chemicals, attempting to sort out those that show promise of arresting or destroying tumor growth. In 1956 drugs and surgery were tried together against cancer of the lung and breast. One such drug, methotrexate, was the first credited with five-year survival of patients suffering from choriocarcinoma, a form of cancer common to ovaries and testicles.[4] But to demonstrate the complexity of the problem, this same drug also may *cause* cancer. It is commonly used to treat psoriasis, the noncancerous but disfiguring skin disease. In 1971 two Memphis dermatologists, S. R. Craig and E. W. Rosenberg, reported they had found cancer in two psoriasis patients who had received methotrexate. Since it belongs to a group of drugs that interfere with cell metabolism, the doctors speculated that it may reduce the body's natural immunity to disease and thus permit cancer to invade.[5]

More than a score of chemical substances have been discovered to aid the war against cancer by exerting some control on multiplication of malignant cells. Some of these inhibit the growth of dividing cells by a process known as alkylation. Others interfere with biochemical pathways involving the action of vitamins, pyrimidines, or folic acid, all of which are vital to growth. Hormone therapy includes the use of the female sex hormone to control cancer of the male prostate gland. Antibiotics and some alkaloid drugs have also been found helpful.

One example of cancer now beginning to dwindle before chemical treatment is Burkitt's lymphoma. Common among African children, this disease produces gross tumors of the jaws and at other sites. Once inevitably fatal in its spread through equatorial regions, 16 to 20 percent of all cases are now curable by drugs.[6]

Disease that strikes down children always seems more repugnant than death in older people. Though not limited to children, one of these is leukemia. It consists of malignant and uncontrolled growth of white blood cells. Any one of four kinds may be acute or chronic. In the acute form a child may be stricken suddenly and waste away to death within a few months.

Because of this threat, leukemia spurred an intense search for a cure, out of which has come one of the more spectacular successes in the war against cancer. Pharmacologists had known of a class of drugs known as *Vinca* alkaloids (two are vinblastin and vincristin), which are extracted from the periwinkle plant, a low-growing evergreen flowering shrub. In 1962 these drugs were found to be effective against acute leukemia, especially when combined with other drugs.[7] By 1965 doctors were able to slow the disease in 90 percent of afflicted children. Without treatment only 5 percent of stricken children survive a year. With drug treatment sixty known victims in 1965 had been free of the disease for five years.[8]

But this was far short of a reliable cure. The search went on, delving into the core of the cell where life is sustained and cancer destroys it. In 1967 it was learned that certain cancers cannot grow without the amino acid asparagine and that its formation could be blocked by the naturally occurring enzyme asparaginase. The beauty of this discovery lay in its suggestion of substances that could starve cancer cells without harming adjacent healthy tissue.

Asparaginase also has proven *not* to be the perfect answer, but by 1970 it had stopped certain types of leukemia, at least temporarily, in 50 percent of the cases where it was tried.[9] Today there are more than two hundred known leukemia victims who have been free of the disease for five years or longer. Before the advent of drug treatment 70 percent of leukemia victims were dead within two months after diagnosis, and most of the rest died shortly thereafter.

Various drug combinations are now credited with some cures in about seven forms of cancer: choriocarcinoma, Burkitt's lymphoma, Ewing's sarcoma, Wilms's tumor, embryonal testicular cancer, Hodgkin's disease, and the leukemias. By no means are all victims cured, and together the seven forms account for only 15 percent of all cancers.[10]

Some prospects for cancer therapy appear to be shunted onto side tracks when new lines of research gain popularity. One of these is the theory of Dr. Albert Szent-Gyorgyi, twice winner of the Nobel Prize in medicine and director of the Institute for Muscle Research, Woods Hole, Massachusetts. He believes cancer may be caused by an inborn enzyme defect which may be treated with an extract of calf liver. Experiments with mice have convinced Dr. Szent-Gyorgyi that the uncontrolled growth of cells is prevented in normal tissue by adequate amounts of chemicals called ketone aldehydes. In some humans production of these chemicals may be prevented by a defect in the proper enzyme.

"From calf liver this can be produced on a big scale in sufficient purity to be administered to humans in a quantity which can be expected to suppress cancer growth," Szent-Gyorgyi said. However, no human trials have been attempted, and he said his research has been hampered by a lack of funds.[11] Although the elderly Hungarian may be a maverick departing from today's mainstream of cancer research, his ideas may eventually fit into the pattern of chemotherapy.

With all the progress made in cancer treatment the greatest step to cure is still early detection. Most cancers can be removed or arrested if they are found soon enough, but most of the time they do not signal their presence until they have grown and spread beyond control. Regular physical examinations can reveal many signs of abnormal growth, but people usually do not see a doctor until something hurts. Then it may be too late. On the other hand, some tools for cancer detection have lain unnoticed on the shelf of their discovery.

One of these is the now-famous "Pap" test. In 1928 George Papanicolaou reported that cells sloughed off or shed from the female cervix could be stained and studied under a microscope. A few cells taken periodically from the entrance to the womb thus can reveal if they are changing in a way indicative of cancer. Papanicolaou's findings were ignored until 1950. After that, however, the American Cancer Society established clinics where the simple test could be performed. Women were advised again and again to have a Pap smear taken. In 1962 the American Medical Association passed a resolution stating that Papanicolaou's work "represents the most significant discovery of the 20th century in early cancer detection. Scores of thousands around the world owe their very lives to his work."[12]

As a result, uterine cancer has declined dramatically in the past two decades, but not as much as it could. Some 42,000 new cases are diagnosed each year, and the 13,000 women who die of it annually could have been saved. Doctors point out that cancer of the uterus is 100 percent curable if every adult woman would have an annual Pap test to detect early signs.[13]

Early detection, drugs, radiation, and surgery now work together in the agonizingly slow war to pinch off the spread of other malignancy. Progress is sometimes visible only by checking history. In 1900 only one out of every six cancer patients was cured. Today the rate is one out of three. Dr. Justin J. Stein, professor of radiology at the University of California in Los Angeles, sees hope that the cure rate will soon be one out of two.[14] That day will be hastened when we can understand the basic causes. Cancer is not spread, except in rare cases, from one person to another. Likewise, only a few forms are passed from one generation to another by heredity.

Although the basic mechanism is still not understood, researchers have established that hundreds of chemicals in the environment may trigger the onset of malignancy. In this sense cancer may be "caused" by substances ranging from asbestos dust to certain drugs and artificial materials added to food.

The first positive identification of a chemical cause came from Percival Pott, the noted London surgeon, in 1775. He noticed that a high percentage of chimney sweeps, young boys indentured to clean the coal-burning flues of London homes, suffered cancer of the scrotum from exposure to the soot. Pott's account of the misery and virtual slavery of the poor "climbing boys" led to the Chimney Sweepers Act of 1788 and many subsequent efforts to eliminate the profession. Despite this, however, there is a record of one child of seven and a half years who was lifted into a chimney as late as 1872, and deaths from this form of cancer remained high in 1902.[15]

Following this evidence that by-products of burning can trigger malignancy, some doctors also suspected tobacco-smoking as a cause. However, it has been only in the past dozen years that systematic studies have branded cigarettes as the prime factor in the growing epidemic of lung cancer. According to Dr. Dan Horn, director of the National Clearing-house for Smoking and Health, at least 15 percent of *all* cancers are related to cigarette-smoking. These include malignancy not only of the lung but also of the larynx, esophagus, bladder, mouth, and possibly some pancreatic cancers.

The lung-cancer toll has been higher among men than women, apparently because men have smoked longer and more heavily, but the statistics are beginning to catch up with women. A recent study showed that the lung-cancer death rate among women who smoke cigarettes is 2 times higher than in nonsmokers. Among women who smoke two or more packs a day the rate is 4.43 times higher. Much counterpropaganda has been based on the fact that smoking and cancer are linked only circumstantially. Doctors still do not know *how* smoking causes cancer, but the evidence grows stronger each year. Late polls indicate the danger has broken the habit for thousands of middle-aged people, but by 1972 there was evidence that overall smoking was on the increase, especially among young people.

About 1,000 chemicals are known to cause cancer in animals, and about 20 so far have been identified in human malignancies. Since society is exposed to about 200,000 new artificial agents each year, scientists are concerned that many may be cancer-causing.[16] In addition to drugs and other substances taken voluntarily, people are exposed to rising pollution in the air and water of such complex chemical mixtures that we are only beginning to understand the harm they may cause.

Remaining is the basic question of how a carcinogen transforms a healthy cell to a malignant one. In 1971 two biochemists at the University of California in Berkeley found part of the answer in working with benzo-a-pyrene, the most common carcinogen found in burning. It is produced in cigarette smoke, auto exhaust, and smoke from industry and electric power plants. Some one thousand tons of this substance are discharged into the atmosphere of the United States every year.

Nobel prize winner Melvin Calvin and Ercole Cavalieri established that benzo-a-pyrene attacks the cells only in the presence of light or oxygen or both. The next step is to determine precisely what part of the cell is attacked. They expect it to be the DNA, central carrier of genetic knowledge. How the genes are altered to relinquish their normal package of replicating information and begin functioning with abnormal instructions is the heart of the cancer question.

The central dogma of genetics postulated that cell-division information could move only outward from the DNA genes to RNA messengers and to manufacture of proteins, but now it appears that the process also works in reverse. Cancerous information may come into the cell by way of RNA, which then alters the DNA, causing the uncontrolled growth of wild new cells.

That theory points to one of the most promising but puzzling leads in modern cancer research—the probability that a virus or viruses may give rise to malignancy. Dr. Carl G. Baker, director of the National Cancer Institute, in 1971 called work with tumor viruses "the biggest thing in sight." Of some 500 known viruses, 110 cause cancer in animals. Most are RNA viruses, and it was recently found that this type is capable of making new DNA if a certain enzyme is present.[17]

This is supported by the findings of Dr. Marcel Baluda, a U.C.L.A. Medical School virologist. He worked with the virus that causes four different tumors in chickens, two forms of leukemia, bone cancer, and kidney tumor. The basis of cancer, he believes, is a large piece of alien genetic information introduced into the cell by a virus. By his theory the RNA tumor virus makes a DNA template that not only reproduces more viruses but also provides new genetic information to the infected cell. This way the cell would lose its specific function of making blood, bone, kidney, or other organs and become cancerous.[18]

The most frustrating facet in viral research is the difficulty encountered in translating research from animals to humans. Though many cancer-causing viruses are found in animals, it has been difficult to isolate virus material in human tumors and prove the relationship. Dozens of research teams around the world have been working on this problem, a situation that sparked fireworks among several who seemed to have come upon proof of a human cancer virus at about the same time late in 1971.

The first report came from Dr. Leon Dmochowsky and Professor Elizabeth S. Priori at the University of Texas in Houston. They announced that a human cell culture, taken from a five-year-old African child who died of Burkitt's lymphoma, continuously produces virus particles in great numbers. The particles are an RNA virus known as type C. "The availability of this virus provides a tool of great potential for investigations of the role of viruses in human cancer," Dr. Dmochowsky said, "and perhaps even for vaccination studies."[19]

Other scientists disputed the Houston team's claim to have isolated a human cancer virus, but later another team at the University of Southern California announced they were "optimistic but cautious" about a similar find. This virus, known as RD 114, was found by Dr. Robert M. McAllister and Dr. Murray B. Gardner in a cell culture taken from a child who died in 1968 of cancer.

"If RD 114 is human, it will put us a light year ahead [in the fight against cancer]," said Dr. Robert J. Huebner, of the National Cancer Institute. "We will be working with humans instead of cats and chickens. We didn't expect to be there for quite a few years."

Still another team, at Georgetown University, reported

finding and culturing a virus from cells taken from a sarcoma (a malignant tumor of connective tissue) from the thigh of a thirty-eight-year-old woman.[20] Whether any or all of these finds turn out to be genuine cancer-causing viruses is still being tested, but they do offer hope for isolating and attacking the root cause.

It is that vision, of someday finding a vaccine or family of vaccines against cancer, that makes the viral theory of causation so attractive. In fact, it seems too simple to many scientists who are still not convinced. Such men warn that the trail to cancer cure or prevention remains more complex than pinning down a virus.

Others believe they are beginning to see light leading toward a unified theory of malignancy. According to Huebner and George Todaro, of the National Cancer Institute, every cell in the body may contain the gene of a virus which is normally kept dormant but which at any time for a variety of reasons may break out and become active. When it does so, it may transform a cell from a well-regulated member of society into a malignant cancer cell. The C-type viruses, isolated in the human cancer cultures, were first shown to cause cancer in chickens sixty years ago. They have since been found in mice, hamsters, cats, and man.

The institute scientists suggest that every vertebrate animal is born with C-type virus genes dormant in their cells, inherited from their parents, but normally kept quiet by a repressor of some sort made by the cells. By this theory the basic cause of cancer is failure of the cell's natural repressor to keep the critical cancer-inducing gene switched off. This failure might occur because of a mutation in the cell or by action of any of the known cancer-causing agents such as chemicals, radiation, or infection by other viruses. Huebner and Todaro also point out that chances of failure in this repressing mechanism would be expected to increase with age, thus explaining the greater incidence of cancer as people grow older and the body mechanism begins to malfunction.

The seed mechanism for the C-type virus has been found in mice, chickens, and cats. Full-grown virus from genetic ingredients has been seen by electron microscope in tumor cells from snakes, a number of animals, and humans, supporting the view of the two men that it is universal among vertebrates. Previous theories regarding virus and cancer assumed that the virus attack came from *outside* the body. In contrast, the new concept holds that the potential seeds for cancer-causing virus are transmitted from parent to offspring and from cell to cell as part of normal inheritance. If this is true, then cancer must be regarded as a natural biological event.

If the supposition holds up in the fire of experimentation, it offers hope that the repressors can be identified, isolated, and perhaps synthesized. It would then follow that an injection of this repressor might help cells maintain control over the dormant virus or help them regain the upper hand if cancerous growth already had begun.[21]

The puzzle of how an RNA virus can come alive and give new instructions to the DNA genes of a cell was partially solved by Dr. Howard Temin at Wisconsin University. He found at least one enzyme that apparently can do the job. Known as reverse transcriptase, the enzyme was found in cancer cells and appeared to have the ability to clip or alter the DNA chain so that the cancer information could be incorporated.[22] If such an enzyme (or many enzymes) is the cancer trigger, perhaps the transformation of cells to cancerous form also could be reversed.

This point was made by Renato Dulbecco and Walter Eckhart, of the Salk Institute at San Diego, California. They pointed out that virologists have now established that viral DNA is present inside virus-transformed cancer cells in an uninfectious form, firmly attached to the chromosomes. Two viruses so far identified are so small that they code for only ten proteins (a task which is simple compared to that performed by most genes or groups of genes). Therefore, the two men said, there is a chance of pinning down the mechanism of cell transformation to a small number of genes, or perhaps just one.

The ability to reverse the action of cancer cells was reported by researchers at New York Hospital's Cornell Medical Center. Dr. Selma Silagi and Sarah Ann Bruce added a chemical called BUdR (5bromodeosyuridine) to tissue cultures containing cells of melanoma, a common and often fatal cancer. The drug BUdR had been known to enter the DNA of cells. When it entered melanoma cells taken from mice, the cells stopped growing in round, many-layered colonies typical of malignancy and began to grow in flat, single-layered groups. When the drug-treated cancer culture was injected into other mice, it failed to produce new tumors.[23]

Dulbecco and Eckhart at San Diego believe it will be ten more years before we have a general understanding of cancer, and perhaps another ten years before effective therapy will be in general use.[24]

Other investigators caution against hasty conclusions. In London D. A. Gilbert warned that "even if a cancer-specific gene is responsible, it is by no means clear how its presence accounts for the many forms of the disease, or the many complex facets that each presents.

"If viruses are *not* unique carcinogenic agents, as I believe," Gilbert added, "then it would seem that we must invoke a mechanism of transformation that is less rigid. The living cell, and especially that which is proliferating, is a dynamic entity in which the levels of components vary in a complex manner. . . . To over-emphasize the role of one contributing factor is liable to hinder a better understanding of both normal and pathological cellular processes."[25]

His argument, simply put, is that no doors should be shut until all answers are known. Cancer may be caused by irritation, by chemicals, by virus, by hormones or their lack, or possibly by unknown combinations of these and other factors. And hovering above all is the growing awareness that the body's immunological system plays a strong role in determining whether or not a person suffers cancer. This is the system of antibodies that protects against infectious disease and which surgeons attempt to suppress temporarily to prevent rejection of newly transplanted organs. Organ transplants were highly instrumental in turning cancer researchers to deeper investigation of the immune system.

Dr. Thomas E. Starzl, transplant surgeon at the Colorado Medical School in Denver, found that 15 out of 2,550 recipients of kidney transplants later developed cancer. Nine occurred in the lymphatic system, which produces the defending cells responsible for tissue rejection. The rest suffered other forms such as cancer of the cervix and skin. At least 10 of the patients have died. All were receiving drugs to suppress immunity at the time they developed cancer. These drugs included Imuran, steroids, and antilymphocyte serum. Though the number of cancer cases is small, the incidence is higher than normally occurs in the general population.[26] Evidence is strong that as the immunity system is weakened, it opens the door for cancer.

This suspicion is supported by Dr. Robert A. Good at the University of Minnesota School of Medicine. He told an American Cancer Society seminar of a twelve-year-old girl who suffered cancer of the ovary after a kidney transplant. Eventually she resisted the anti-immunity drugs, rejected the kidney, and died, but an autopsy showed that the cancer had disappeared. This implied that when the girl became resistant to the drug, her production of lymphocytes bounced back and rejected not only the foreign kidney but the foreign tumor as well.

Dr. Good is one of many who now believe that every person may get cancer many times during a lifetime but that it is usually stopped by the immunity system before the tumor can grow very large. Cancer would develop only when part of the body's immune mechanism is absent or functioning at low ebb. An authority on the evolution of the immune system, Good believes that cancer is a basic tool of nature to protect a species against the dangers of overcrowding and exploding population.

He terms this a process of programmed death. The lymphoid system to fight infection is active in youth and less active in old age, giving more survival value to the young and less to the aged. "Ultimately we will find a way to control this immune system to suit our needs," Dr. Good said, "but we should not forget that it took 300 million years for nature to devise the present system."[27]

Many researchers have followed this suggested pathway to cancer control. Dr. Loren J. Humphrey, of the Emory University School of Medicine in Atlanta, has developed an experimental tumor "vaccine" prepared from cancer tissue removed during surgery in a unique partnership arrangement. The preparation is designed to concentrate the specific antigens that make cancerous tissue different from normal cells and thus trigger the immunity response. Patients are paired, each receiving tumor material from the other's cancer in a series of inoculations. Theoretically, each patient produces white blood cells sensitive to his partner's tumor in response to the vaccination. Hopefully, these white cells will attack the cancer when administered back to the patient who provided the tumor material. Humphrey said he has used the procedure only on patients whose cancer has spread too far to be halted by surgery or radiation. Among forty-two patients tumors shrank in response to this therapy. In four others the tumors stopped growing.

Dr. Humphrey recognizes that inoculating a patient with cancerous tissue risks inducing a new cancer. To skirt this danger, Dr. Charles F. McKhann, of the University of Minnesota, developed a way to create "immune" white cells outside the body. In his method tumor cells are grown in laboratory cultures and then brewed with white cells from the patient's lymph system. In theory the killer white cells would multiply and gain power against the specific cancer tissue. Later this material is injected back into the patient to stimulate his own immunity.[28]

Researchers hope that stimulating the body's natural defense may at least be helpful in cleaning up cancer cells which may remain after a tumor has been removed by surgery. This approach is being followed at U.C.L.A.'s Medical Center under a program sponsored by the National Cancer Institute. According to Dr. Donald Morton, professor of surgery and chief of oncology (cancer studies), patients who recover from cancer surgery are given additional chemical therapy to help prevent recurrence. These patients receive a vaccine made of parts of their own tumor plus a drug called BCG. This drug has been used against tuberculosis in many parts of the world, and tuberculosis patients so treated show a lower than normal inclination to develop leukemia. Apparently BCG stimulates the immune system and may strengthen a person against malignancy.

In 1972 Dr. Morton announced that by culturing cancer cells with a patient's lymphocytes he has increased their power to kill tumor cells by a factor of 10. He believes an injection of these reinforced natural defenders will mean the difference between short-term and long-term survival in cancer patients. Morton also developed a test to measure how well a patient's immune system is working. This can tell which will have the best chance of avoiding cancer recurrence.

Dr. Morton has also found that building a serum with strong cancer antibodies is best accomplished by taking the lymphocytes from a near family member of the victim. This is based on indications that sarcoma-type cancer is caused by a virus that is shared by the family members. Not all fall victim to it, which suggests they may be protected by their lymphocytes. Thus a powerful vaccination of these, from a relative, may help the cancer victim.[29]

James Gowans, of Oxford University in England, believes tumors are able to establish themselves only by developing their own antibodies that save them from killer lymphocytes in the bloodstream. If this is true, then it may be possible to block a tumor's antibodies, allowing the body's defense to go about its business of rejecting the cancer.[30]

Another promising approach to the control of cancer emerged in 1972 from Children's Hospital Medical Center in Boston. Dr. Judah Folkman, a professor at Harvard Medical School, said that cancers may be kept dormant by denying them access to blood supply.

He pointed out that a cancer, regardless of how it starts, cannot grow larger than a BB shot unless it gets its own blood supply. It does this by sending out a special chemical signal which causes capillaries, the body's tiniest blood vessels, to grow toward and then into the cancer. After that happens, the cancer is free to grow unlimited.

Dr. Folkman and associates have isolated what they call the tumor angiogenesis factor (TAF), which is the chemical produced by cancers to stimulate capillary growth. If this factor can be blocked out, which Dr. Folkman believes may be possible within two to five years, cancers could be kept small, and large ones shrunk by the absence of enough blood to help them grow.[31]

Other scientists have attempted to identify the sort of person most likely to develop cancer. Dr. Claus Bahnson, of the Eastern Pennsylvania Psychiatric Institute in Philadelphia, believes the most cancer-prone person is an "inoffensive good guy everybody likes because he never tells them off." In a study of five hundred cancer patients he found a tendency to bottle up emotions and an inability to handle unpleasant emotions such as anxiety, depression, anger, and guilt.

Dr. George F. Solomon, Stanford University psychiatrist, believes this relationship with cancer is due to a tie-in with hormones. Such people tend to build up levels of adrenocortical hormones (the so-called stress hormones), which tend to suppress the body's immune system. With the defense down, cancer then can get a foothold. This view was supported by Dr. Elena A. Kornevac in Russia, who found that a portion of the hypothalamus is involved in the functioning of the immune system. Electrical stimulation of this part of the brain increases an animal's ability to make antibodies against disease.[32]

So now the many fragments of cancer research begin to coalesce into an outline of the larger puzzle. Many pieces are still missing while we learn more about essential life processes. President Nixon in 1971 asked Congress to appropriate $100,000,000 in addition to $230,000,000 already allocated to the National Cancer Institute to intensify the war against malignancy. Dr. Baker, director of the institute, anticipates $1,000,000,000 in funds by 1976 and is staffing to coordinate research, but he does not anticipate a quick victory. He visualizes a reliable cure, perhaps, by the year 2000.

Others doubt the efficacy of pouring vast amounts of money into the field. One of these is Dr. Joshua Lederberg, Nobel prize winner and professor of genetics at Stanford.

" 'Cure Cancer,' like all war cries, is an oversimplification and it has some potential for backfiring if unachievable hopes are aroused," Lederberg warned. "We should not dismiss the fact that some $2 billion have already been invested in cancer research during the past twenty years. What is the outcome?

"Earlier diagnosis of certain cancers and new treatment by surgery, radiation, and drugs have indeed reduced the inevitability of dying from cancer, once found. Over two million citizens who have had cancer would not be alive today had they been left untreated. Nevertheless, the aggregate rate of death from cancer is still rising. This is due mainly to the epidemic of lung cancer cases attributable to cigarette smoking and air pollution. Can more money spent on research give us a realistic hope of outpacing these statistics?"

Dr. Lederberg pointed out that the great promise comes from the strides in basic biological knowledge of recent years. One is discovery of the enzyme that codes DNA from RNA in cells of human leukemia and presumably caused by a virus. Other studies on the chemistry of the cell surface have begun to clarify the invasive properties of cancer cells.

"Despite these leads," Dr. Lederberg emphasized, "I believe that 'cancer cure' is a misleading slogan, only because cancer *prevention* is a far more rewarding and promising approach than cure of the disease once established. Prevention also offers the most incisive channels for exploiting basic molecular and cell biology."[33]

There is no question that President Nixon sought prevention as well as cure, but Lederberg and others stress the need to focus attention and resources upon preventing the thousands of cancers that could be headed off by present knowledge. These preventive measures, among other things, could include outlawing tobacco and cleansing our environment of the pollutants that we know can cause malignancies.

Of one thing we may be sure: The war against cancer will be won. What we have accomplished so far is similar to fighting a forest fire around its edges. Soon we will be able to drop new biological bombs on the center of the fire. And when cancer is gone, we also may know some ways to keep from growing old.

CHAPTER 11

Planned Obsolescence

There comes a day—perhaps a chill, damp dawn in autumn—when it is more difficult to spring out of bed and face the work of the world. You feel a twinge of stiffness in a knee or shoulder. Dry skin flakes when you scratch. Sitting on the edge of the bed, mustering strength to meet the day, you contemplate blue veins on ankle or calf and brown pigment spots on the back of your hand.

There has been a change in the weather, you note absently, signaled by soreness in the pink slash of scar where the gall bladder came out last year. (Or perhaps it was a hysterectomy, although they're doing that another way now so it doesn't leave a blemishing scar to remind a woman of the passing years.) The gray dawn provides a moment to wonder how high your blood pressure is today, and the cholesterol. You can't quite remember what it was you told yourself last night not to forget this morning.

A bathroom mirror is cruel at dawn. It reveals a roll of fat around the belly, loose skin under the chin, and gray in the stubble before the lather goes on. And when did you last make love to your wife?

The clock of life is slowing down, ticking less firmly, less exuberantly, less accurately.

I am growing old.

Dreary, distressing thought; behind it lies the dread of death. Intellectually we accept the fact that aging and dying are as natural in the universe as birth and life. Emotionally we reject it. We see mothers and fathers, relatives and friends, pass through the declination. We attend a funeral, happy that it is not yet ours. Somewhere in the mind is a mechanism that rationalizes that I am unique, that I (the center of *my* universe) am not really growing old, that I really won't die. But it is only a mechanism to protect us from despair. The fact that the hour of our death is hidden provides the only motivation to keep us working and planning for the future. Many sociologists, in fact, declare that as long as a man or a woman continues to plan how he will spend tomorrow or next year, that person is not really old. The aged are those who wait and plan for nothing except death. Those eventually pray for it to come.

It is hard to view ourselves objectively. Under dietary restrictions we joke with friends that we didn't really like sugar anyway, that the old machine is beginning to run down, that the arms are growing shorter (with dimming vision), and, wistfully, what a shame it is that the pleasures of youth are wasted on the young. We talk to the encroaching shadows, trying to make friends with God who once seemed so far away, and try to see ourselves as we really are—a small part of nature's planned obsolescence. We must go away, to whatever heaven or hell or nowhere that comes next, to make room for the next generation. With current worries about overcrowding the world, that requirement seems more urgent each day.

The prospect of death somehow seems less frightening and repugnant if we can think of relinquishing our place to a new baby, pink with our blood and blessed with a new span of years to fulfill. Or again, though we may die without really knowing why we lived, at least we know the worn-out husk will go back to the earth to provide food for nature's ceaseless fountain of life. Perhaps this was truly all that was meant so long ago by the mental itch to find the philosophers' stone, the elixir of life, Ponce de León's lost fountain of youth.

Yet when our cells and organs wither away before the onslaught of degenerative disease, we ask: Why must we die? There was the woman in Turkey who claimed in 1963 to be 168 years old, perhaps the oldest person in the world. Mrs. Hatice Nine said she was born in 1795, her claim partially corroborated by the fact that she had a grandson who was 64 and had six grandchildren of his own.[1] Even if she unknowingly exaggerated by as much as thirty years, it was still a ripe old age.

Most communities can now find someone who is one hundred or more. There are more than twelve thousand such people in the United States today. As to that arbitrary and foolish dividing line—age sixty-five—which tumbles a man willy-nilly from usefulness to retirement, this is the mythical age at which men and women are doomed by the artificialities of society to join the class of the aged, whether they are ready or not. This class of people is growing rapidly. In 1900 there were three million Americans sixty-five and older. Today there are nearly twenty million; by 1980 there will be twenty-four million.

So death *is* coming later to us, on the average, than it did to our ancestors. Six out of each ten thousand people in the United States live to be one hundred or more. One out of ten is sixty-five or older. Is it possible for the medical and biological sciences to find ways to help us all reach sixty-five, seventy, or even one hundred? Though the odds are high against achieving one hundred, there are many things we can do now, and others we may do in the future, to extend the *useful* lives of men and women by a number of years. That number depends to a great degree on how we live.

The Bible promised men a life-span of three score and ten. It is peculiar that this has not changed in two millennia, but it may be that seventy years is the good round number we are intended and *programmed* to live, though that does not account for the exceptions who live longer.

In the past two decades we have taken comfort in the fact that average life expectancy has steadily increased. A baby born at the beginning of this century could expect to live forty-seven years, slightly more for women, slightly less for men. Today it is about sixty-seven for men and seventy-four for women.[2] Almost all of that improvement, however, has come in the control of killer disease among infants, children, and young adults. The additional life expectancy of a man who has reached sixty is little more now than it was fifty years ago. By 1972 there were disquieting signs that under stresses of accelerating change in society, the life expectancy of men was beginning to decline.

"The age of senility today is exactly what it was at the time of Moses," said Dr. Alex Comfort, director of the Medical Research Council Group on Aging at University College in London. "What medicine has achieved so far, in conjunction with social betterment, is to enable more people to reach old age. No amount of conventional effort—cancer research, spare part surgery, or welfare—can do more than re-arrange the distribution of death to make it more common at ages 75 to 80. In privileged societies we already are pushing that limit."[3]

The point was made another way by Thomas L. Lincoln and Palmer T. Van Dyke, of the Rand Corporation: "Now that infections like typhoid fever, pneumococcal pneumonia, tuberculosis, and polio have been largely overcome," the men wrote, "each of us can live long enough to anticipate cancer, stroke, cardiac failure, or some other expensive, debilitating illness of old age."[4]

The list of these is long, but that is enough to tell us what is in store if we live long enough. Perhaps the misery isn't worth it, but the end is almost always postponed by that final desperate struggle for one more day, one more breath.

With present medicine, as Dr. Comfort pointed out, industrialized and prosperous countries may already have reached a temporary limit to the extension of life. In 1970 the World Health Organization reported that heart, lung, and other chronic illnesses had caused the death rates to creep up again after 150 years of steady decline. While the death rate continued to be lower among women than men, in sixteen out of twenty-two countries (including the United States) the death rate increased between 1960 and 1969. Car accidents were listed as an increasingly important cause. So was suicide.[5]

If that were the end of the story, it would be a gloomy one. Fortunately there is more.

Because human life is so long, and the average family no longer stays with one doctor, it is impossible to tell any individual how much longer he might have lived if he had lived differently. People with ancestors who survived long years are likely to do the same, but aside from this, environmental factors play a large part in aging. Any doctor will tell you that if you smoke less, eat less, drink less, and exercise more, you will live longer years in good health. Most tend to ignore this advice because it requires effort. We would prefer a handy-dandy pill to take care of the matter for us.

Despite warnings of cancer and other chronic disease, some smokers rationalize their habit, hoping that by the time cancer strikes, medical science will have found a cure. Overweight men and women who relish a slab of pie for dessert will tell themselves this small increment of sugar isn't enough to trigger diabetes and promise to start that diet tomorrow. The beer-drinker plops his sagging belly down in front of the TV and drinks more beer to quiet the nagging voice that tells him he should be out taking a walk or working in the garden. There is a tendency in almost everyone, when a habit or pleasure deprivation is involved, to adopt the fatalistic attitude that no matter how he lives, when his allotted time is up, he'll die.

Obviously, there may come a time in any person's life when he makes the free choice to indulge in dwindling pleasures at the expense of a few more days which might be added to the end of his life. Many, when deprived of everything they enjoy, would prefer to die. This is true of the aged in senility who cling to the thread of physical existence only by drugs, infusions, or mechanical devices. So what we seek is *not* just an extension of days, but more days of healthy, useful life.

Gerontologists who study the process of aging generally agree that most people could add five to ten more useful years by improving their living habits. As Charles Dickens wrote in *Barnaby Rudge*: "Father time is not always a hard parent, and, though he tarries for none of his children, often lays his hand lightly on those who have used him well."

This is most true of diet. Dr. Lee H. Schlesinger, of Hines Veterans Hospital in Chicago, reports that a survey of aging patients showed that 50 percent of the men and 47 percent of the women were more than 10 percent overweight. He advised that everyone should decrease calories as the years advance. He recommended that older persons mix dry skim milk or dry yeast into their foods to reduce calorie intake and fat while increasing the protein necessary for the vitality of organs and muscles.[6]

Effects of diet and other factors are difficult to measure over the long human life-span, but spectacular results have been obtained in experiments with lower animals. One of these is the rotifer, an aquatic animal about the size of a pinhead. One might question what relationship this tiny creature could have with man, but the rotifer is an ideal animal for aging experiments. It has no father, and the individuals hatched from mother's eggs have identical genetic life programs.

Normally the rotifer has a life-span of about thirty-four days. The first four are devoted to development. Then comes eleven to fifteen days of active life during which it lays about forty eggs. Finally there are eighteen days of "retirement." Experimenters have found they can increase the rotifer's life from thirty-four to as much as fifty-five days simply by reducing the food supply. A 62-percent increase in life is spectacular enough, but how it is allotted is even more exciting. Food deprivation does not affect the eighteen-day retirement but lengthens the *active life* of the creature. It continues to lay the same number of eggs but takes longer to do it. Experiments with higher animals have produced similar results. The life-span of mice and rats, for example, can be nearly doubled by reducing their diet. One theory of why this may be so is that a constantly hungry animal will constantly seek food. The activity steps up the regulatory secretions of their adrenal glands.

"These experimental conditions cannot be applied to the human," said Dr. Nathan W. Shock, head of the Gerontology Research Center of the National Institutes of Health, "but they are of extreme importance in showing that the genetic pattern of aging can be influenced by environmental factors. As the biologist generates more basic knowledge about the mechanisms of aging, applications which will benefit people will evolve."

Dr. Shock lists environment as the first of four essential factors that limit longevity. Second is degenerative disease. Third is obesity. Fourth is the gradual change in organs and tissues causing a drop in reserve capacity.

"These changes do not proceed uniformly in all organ systems and may or may not be the inevitable consequences of aging," Dr. Shock said. "It is in this area that a great deal of research needs to be done. We do know that many of these changes can be compensated for by prosthetic devices such as glasses, hearing aids, dentures, etc., and that others can be retarded by systematic exercise and activities. Others can be lived with simply by avoiding the strain of excesses."[7]

It is only in the past twenty years that studies of the aged and their problems have been pressed vigorously. Few universities devote attention to these matters, and geriatrics is the poor relation in the funding of scientific research. Dr. Denham Harman, chairman of the American Aging Association, pointed out that the eight million dollars for aging contained in the 1971 budget for the National Institutes of Health is "piddling, compared to sums allotted to negative means of lengthening the life span, such as conquering disease after you've got it."

In a memorandum to members he said: "President Nixon has called for a massive strike against cancer, yet the aging process which ultimately becomes the concern of all, and underlies the increasing susceptibility to cancer and heart disease, has had scant support." Harman feels that aging research, in its present state, offers the possibility of increasing the human life-span by no more than ten or fifteen years. "The research goal," he said, "should be to make long life better, rather than just to make life longer."[8]

One reason why geriatric research has been late coming and slow to proceed lies in a general distaste for the elderly, the feeling that the old should get out of the way to make room for the young. This prejudice is blamed for turning many young scientists away from geriatric research and may even influence the doctor's attitude toward his patients. The Wisconsin Medical Society advised its members to guard against this attitude.

"The younger physician often harbors prejudice and dislike for association with the aged, who probably already is suffering from rejection by others," the society stated. "Hypochondria and body delusions may occur in the senile due to over-concern with bodily functions and anxiety. The aged's attempts to maintain genital potency to satisfy his still-strong sexual urges while physical capacities are diminishing may contribute to his psychological stress. The doctor must appreciate the patient's difficulties and be willing to work with him."[9]

Although aches and pains and the dread of losing physical vigor are severe enough, the most distressing symptom of old age is loss of the capacity to think and remember. An ultimate sadness is invoked by seeing an old person in this vegetative state of senility. The most obvious symptom is depression. Older people worry about being jobless, the lack of money, loss of sexual strength, loneliness, or the fate of a spouse if one should die. Psychiatrists have achieved considerable success in treating depression of the aged with a variety of drugs, from amphetamine to procaine and vitamin B^{12}.

Psychiatrist Francis H. Stern holds out hope that creative aging in the mental sense may soon be possible. Writing in

Psychosomatics, he said mental deterioration is not an inherent part of aging. He cited research showing that memory is more than a biochemical system. Nerve cells continually form new connections and break old ones while producing chemical substances to regulate distant organs. Stern said the brain's production of RNA can be stimulated by combining the drugs pemoline and magnesium hydroxide. This finding could open the way to a new system of medicine based on RNA-mediated memory inside each cell.

"Old age, this mature period of life, has important social and anthropological functions which the world has not recognized and utilized," Stern declared. "There is no uniform pattern of decline in the creative process with chronological age. One should strive not to stay young, but to use youth as a time for learning how to live, acquiring basic knowledge and experience, gaining judgment, and aiming toward the age when wisdom can replace impetuosity. It is our attitude toward age, not age itself, that is the national problem."[10]

Bernard Strehler, professor of biology at the University of Southern California in Los Angeles, believes the greatest block to solving problems of aging is public misinformation. "Progressive senescence in the post-mature years conditions our physical capacities, our sexual lives, our economic and social enterprises," he said. "It also colors our plans, hopes, and dreams. Yet despite this universal awareness of aging, its origin in human cells and molecules is the least-investigated of all our major biological phenomena." Strehler set forth ten "myths" that must be erased from human thinking before realistic goals can be set and met:

Myth No. 1: Man has the ability to become physically immortal.

Based on incomplete understanding of living things, this dream permeates history but ignores the fact that any natural object will gradually become disorganized and cease functioning with passage of time. Because most species evolved under difficult conditions, nature does not allow production of substances that have no additional evolutionary advantages. By this law of frugality, many tissues and cells are not replaced after full development. The human body consists in part of cells that cannot be replaced during later life.

It may be possible to reinstate some of the regenerative capacities lost in evolution. Our storehouse of brain cells at birth is all we ever have, and they are gradually lost through degeneration. Therefore, it would seem that restoring the brain's ability to build new cells would be a good research goal. However, if brain cells were to be replaced, we would lose part of the information stored in the old ones.

"It might be possible for a species to evolve that has acquired or retained some capacity for regenerating all parts as they deteriorate," Strehler said. "Such a species would be essentially immortal, but the circumstances of evolution seem to preclude this option."

Myth No. 2: Man cannot add significantly to his healthy life-span.

Man's development as the dominant creature on earth enabled him to outlive other primates long enough to store and correlate information and modify his behavior during the training period of childhood, adolescence, and maturation.

"But to contend that there is a specific limit to the life span of creatures built on our general body plan is nonsense," Strehler said. "Evolution does not proceed according to predetermined steps with finite goals in mind. Evolution is a cold, impartial process in which the prime factor determining change and success is the probability of transmitting one's genes to future generations."

Once the reproductive years are past and children are reared, nature seems to lose interest in the individual. Apparently we really are programmed in the genetic code for planned obsolescence. If this is true, it may be possible to change the programming. "There is no sound basis for believing either that man has achieved his ultimate limit of evolvable longevity," Strehler added, "or that his present genes are not subject to environmental manipulation to give him many additional years of healthy middle life."

Myth No. 3: Much greater healthy longevity can be achieved but not in the near future.

"If the results obtained on experimental animals also apply to the human species," Strehler said, "the extension of healthy years for an additional *15 to 25 years* is within reach."

One way is reduction of fat. Another is the use of antioxidant drugs, such as vitamin E, which has increased the lives of laboratory rats. In Europe experimenters are working with "rejuvenating" substances ranging from procaine to nucleic acid derivatives known as antireticulocytotoxic serums, though these have not yet proved effective.

Another way to increase life is to cool body temperature. With the rotifers, cooling their water caused them to live longer. The life-span of fish is increased in cold lakes. Mice and bats which hibernate (during which life processes are slowed) live up to four times longer than similar creatures that don't. Strehler pointed out that human body temperature fluctuates about a degree on a daily basis. "A decrease in temperature of two to three degrees is likely to have no noticeably adverse effect," he said, "and this small decrease would be expected to add about 20 to 30 useful years to the life span."

Myth No. 4: The postponement of senescence will impose great economic burdens on society.

This argument says old people are a burden and therefore should be cleared out as quickly as possible. It contends that if people live longer, they will require more medical care, more services, more housing, and allocation of more resources to an unproductive group. The truth is that measures available to increase life would also improve health. With ailments and anxieties postponed or removed, aging people could continue productive in society for a longer period.

Myth No. 5: An extended life-span will pose difficult new social problems.

This postulates that a greater fraction of older people would conflict with younger age groups and form a political force to extract new benefits from society. This is not likely because extension of healthy life would also extend the years of "young in mind." Attitudes and physical condition are not set by age but by the realities of existence.

"Consider the opportunities for new self-development that a period of forty-or-so years of healthy and vigorous life following child-rearing would afford for mothers," Strehler suggested. "Consider the opportunities for further training and an extended productive period which would open for the father, and the benefits of having physically young grandparents and even great-grandparents available for benign instruction of children."

Myth No. 6: An extended life-span will add to the difficulties produced by man's major enemy—the population explosion.

This myth ignores the fact that healthy people of greater age could contribute to an increase in total resources as well as the quality of existence. A greater danger than old people is the birth of a disproportionate number of people with lower learning and productive capacity.

"If an increasing fraction of the population is incapable of contributing to its own maintenance," Strehler commented, "then even in the zero population growth situation the future becomes dismal to contemplate. Genetic limitations in our gene pools are a real danger, but increased longevity is a potential boon."

Myth No. 7: We ought not tinker with aging, because the way it is now is the way nature is.

This myth ranks with the argument that if God had intended men to fly, He would have given us wings. James Bonner at Cal Tech tells of the lady in Pasadena who argued that if God had intended men to fly in jets, He would have had the Wright Brothers invent them. Nature is always changing. If we had not already tinkered with her ways, none of the healing arts would now exist.

Myth No. 8: Aging is desirable; it confers values upon those who possess it that are unattainable without it, and it permits the production of more highly evolved forms of life.

This is a rationalization. The elderly derive their value from experience, not from physical deterioration. As for evolution, there is no evidence aging does anything but reduce the individual's ability to reproduce.

Myth No. 9: Increasing the life-span of the human will result in our being surrounded by an increased percentage of decrepit, unsightly, dependent persons.

This is not true. One cannot prolong life without increasing the level of health and therefore comeliness and self-reliance at all ages, unless we spend more useless funds to keep useless hulks alive.

Myth No. 10: Present research efforts are adequate. Progress being made is about all that can be expected.

Strehler calls the small amount being spent in the United States on aging and its remedies a scandal of neglect. "Aging research," he declared, "will yield answers that will improve the well-being and productive life of every single human being now under the age of fifty. It stands out as the great blind spot in national research objectives and planning."[11]

Funds may be short, but not everyone is blind to the progress that is possible. One of the most prominent is Dr. Shock at Baltimore, who established the Select Society for Seeking Scientists, Saints, and Sinners (with a seventh "S" added for Sisters). This society never has a group meeting. There are no minutes or dues. The only requisite for membership is a person's willingness to spend three days in a hospital every year or eighteen months having blood tests, walking up and down stairs, breathing into tubes, and exercising. The Seven S's may be the most thorough study undertaken of the human aging process, and no one knows when the study will end.

Dr. Shock began it in 1958 with one hundred healthy, educated men. Before that time, traditional aging studies compared the physiology and reactions of young lab assistants and medical students with those of old, poor inhabitants of chronic disease wards and old-age homes. Any differences were automatically assigned to aging, disregarding variances in environment and other factors. Dr. Shock believed more valid results could be obtained by studying one population group, comparing age differences, and testing for changes with time. The society now contains more than six hundred volunteers who have been tested at least once and ten who have been tested eight times. They range in age from eighteen to ninety-nine.

"Our approach has been to take in adults of all ages and follow them as long as we can," said Arthur Norris, coordinator of the program. "In doing that at least we know what happens to selected twenty-year-olds as they move to age thirty, and to thirty-year-olds as they move to age forty. This way we can have a cross-sectional study, in which we can describe age differences right away, and a longitudinal study, whose results demand patience. After ten or fifteen years we begin to find out how each individual changes with age and how each physiological system in that person ages."

Dr. Shock foresees the program going on indefinitely, perhaps for generations, if the impetus can be maintained, because only the long term can reveal what happens to a man or woman from youth to death. Already some general results and answers have emerged. Most people believe that when an adult reaches maturity, there is a long period of stability and then a sudden decline in the later years. The Shock program has shown rather that most changes seem to be gradual and progressive. The body dies a little every day.

The study also showed the need to revise some standards once considered normal. As people grow older, their systems change. What is normal for a seventy-year-old body may not be normal for a twenty-year-old. Sugar tolerance is a good example. In the aged this tolerance declines so drastically that if common standards were applied, nearly 50 percent of all elderly persons would be classified as diabetics. This is not the case, so doctors are revising the standards while seeking answers to why the glucose tolerance declines with age.

The ability to work or exercise falls rapidly with the years. Endurance and strength drop from 20 to 40 percent between ages thirty-five and ninety. This is because muscles at work need extra oxygen. With aging, the heart cannot step up its pace as well as a young person's, and the amount of oxygen the blood can absorb from the lungs also falls. Air that can be moved through the lungs declines about 40 percent between ages twenty and eighty. Another companion of aging is a drop in reserve capacities, the ability of an organ to return to its resting condition after a disturbance. Heart tests showed that the work capacity of eighty-year-olds under a two-minute recovery requirement is 60 percent less than that of a twenty-year-old.

"There are many questions we won't get a grip on for years," Dr. Shock said. "I don't expect to be around for all or many of them. That is what gerontology is, you see. Longitudinal studies of man may require generations of observers. Some of the big questions we have to decide now are methodological, so that in the year 2070 the scientists don't have to worry over what our records of diagnoses and observations mean."

As it identifies more clearly how aging occurs, the Shock program will also cast more illumination on the question of *why*. The deeper we look, the more it appears that the predestination of religion may have a biological equivalent. Dr. Charles H. Barrows at Johns Hopkins University, the man who pioneered the study of rotifers, points out there are four main theories of aging.

The oldest—and least substantiated—states that each cell is endowed from conception with a fixed amount of vital substance which is used up as time passes. When the substance is gone, the cell dies. When enough cells die, the body dies. The problem is that no such "vital substance" has been identified.

A corollary idea suggests that damaging substances accumulate in the cell and interfere with its normal function. Although an insoluble substance called age pigment, or lipofuscin, is found in old tissues, such as in the heart, the brain, and the adrenal glands, no one has established a relationship with cell function reduction.

The third theory focuses upon the genetic material in the cell. It postulates that as the years pass, alterations or errors occur in the cell's DNA molecule which cause it to transmit erroneous information to the next generation of cells. This also would produce defective enzymes multiplying with time. Ultimately, the cell—and the organism—would die. Dr. Barrows said that so far it has not been demonstrated that such errors actually develop naturally in a cell's life.

The fourth theory—and the one most widely accepted—is that the genetic machinery is programmed from the beginning to slow gradually and stop operating at a predestined point in time.

"All four theories could be correct," Dr. Barrows said. "The genetic program could be the underlying reason for the changes noted by other theories." (If the program theory is proved, he warned, no quick increase in man's life-span should be expected.) "We might learn to slow the aging process and we might not. Even if we did learn to do so, I'm sure it wouldn't be as simple as writing a new program for a computer."[12]

In view of the anxious life-wish of the aged, Dr. Barrow's conservatism is wise. Others are more optimistic.

"Aging and death are not inevitable," said Desmond King-Hele, of the Royal Aircraft Establishment in England. "Death is merely a convenient evolutionary invention to clear away creatures that cannot improve and make room for new generations. Biological prediction is often too timid. Immortality may be just around the corner, but at present we seem bent upon trying to kill ourselves by polluting our environment."[13]

A moderate view is taken by Dr. Comfort in London. He points out that age one hundred or thereabouts represents a biological "wall" beyond which most men cannot go with any foreseeable advance in the cure or prevention of specific diseases, including cancer and heart ailments. "At the same time," he said, "the high stability of the rate of vigor loss in every species investigated so far suggests that there is a clock or clocks [that control aging], and that by tampering with this mechanism the timing of degenerative changes could be altered, not just piecemeal, but across the board. The conviction that such a project is worthwhile has grown steadily over the past twenty years."

Dr. Comfort made the following predictions:

1. That given some "decent" human experimentation, we shall know by 1990 of at least one proven way of extending vigorous life by about 20 percent.

2. That the most likely agents will be simple and cheap and will not depend on organ grafts or elaborate care units.

3. That the direct application of such research will be worldwide.

4. That all existing medical services and governments will elect to apply it or at least be unable to prevent its application.[14]

Dr. Bonner at Cal Tech elaborates upon Comfort's suggestion that it may become possible to "tinker" with the specific genes that contain the timing mechanism of aging. He referred to the discovery of chromosomal RNA, which plays a key role in deciding which genes shall be active in a cell at a certain time. "It should be possible before too long to isolate or synthesize the specific chromosomal RNA needed to change a cell's function in a predictable way," he said.

One goal might be restoring the brain cell's lost capacity to replace itself. Though 100,000 cells are lost each day after age thirty-five, Dr. Bonner said there are still enough cells in the brain to last three hundred years, but mental sharpness decreases the older a person gets. If new cells could be produced, Bonner pointed out, they would have to be trained, because they would not contain memory. A person might have to spend much of his time in school to keep up with his increasing brainpower. Within ten to fifteen years, Bonner predicted, there should exist the scientific basis for men to direct the growth of any organ desired.

This prospect is based on study of lower creatures, some of

which are able to regrow a lost tail (as in some lizards). It is also indicated by a base of growing knowledge of cell differentiation and the mechanisms by which genes are "uncovered" to perform their specific work and then order work to stop when a bone, arm, or fingernail is fully formed.

In theory, if cells once were programmed to build an arm, then conceivably if an arm is lost, cells in remaining tissue could be reinstructed to repeat the original work of creation. By gene manipulation we might thus be able to grow a new heart, a liver, or even a lost leg. And the same mechanism might be used to "reset" the genes of cancer cells so they would die or revert to their normal noncancerous state of replication.[15]

While such bright promise is offered to middle-agers everywhere, the opposite note of euthanasia was sounded by Dr. Kenneth O. A. Vickery, of England. He told a congress of the Royal Society of Health in London that the time has come when doctors should stop striving by intensive methods to keep elderly patients alive. He said geriatric patients threaten to overload many hospitals.

"To a Christian nation," Vickery said, "serious consideration of euthanasia [allowing patients to die] should be unthinkable, but in a community which can no longer nurse all its chronic sick and where beds are so blocked by the aged that younger people cannot be admitted, we can no longer avoid the issue of medicated survival which, as so successfully manifested in current medical practice, is surely one of the cruelest hazards to which we can be subjected."

Vickery's suggestion aroused a storm of protest. A spokesman for the British Medical Association said: "We cannot agree that there should be any age limit beyond which a doctor's obligation to his patients should be modified." Vickery was fifty-two at the time of his statement. Philosopher Bertrand Russell, then ninety-six, commented: "The doctor clearly is not yet old enough to know better."

On the other hand, Vickery's point was supported by Ernest Melling, general secretary of the National Foundation of Old

Age Pensioners. Melling was eighty-three. "When a person comes near to the time of dying," he said, "he should be left to die. It is a natural thing that when one gets old, death doesn't mean much. If I suddenly became ill and thought I would not get better, I would like to be left to die."

Former President Dwight D. Eisenhower survived seven heart seizures, acute intestinal blockage, and pneumonia before he died at age seventy-eight in March, 1969. His life was extended by the most sophisticated measures known to medical science. "If this is to be the case for the rest of society," Vickery said, "we are in for a hell of a time."[16]

Although euthanasia is still an uneasy thought in general society, it could conceivably become an accepted tool for relieving the world's population congestion. In the meantime some people advocate even more extreme measures for clinging to life.

One of these is the possibility of conditioning the human being to hibernate, possibly for months or years at a time. Such an existence would hardly be living, but it might satisfy the general craving "to stick around to see what happens tomorrow." Experiments in lowering temperatures to slow aging suggest that some form of hibernation might be possible. The discovery that some drugs might also do this was revealed in 1971.

Dr. Harold F. Hardman, of the Medical College of Milwaukee, said that a single injection of a pure form of marijuana put dogs into suspended animation for up to eight days, after which they recovered and were normal. This knowledge came to light after fifteen years of secrecy was lifted by the U.S. Army, which sponsored the research to find a way to "suspend" thousands of persons hurt in a nuclear holocaust until there was time to give them medical attention. Dr. Hardman believes purified marijuana also may relieve pain, lower blood pressure and body temperature, treat migraine headache and epilepsy, and tranquilize patients.[17]

A more extreme manifestation of the human wish for immortality is cryonics, a technique for freezing the body intact after death with the hope that it may be thawed in some future year when medical science has gained the knowledge to repair the cause of fatality. Dr. James H. Bedford, a seventy-three-year-old psychologist who died of lung cancer in 1967, had his body packed in dry ice. The blood was drained and replaced with antifreeze and the body shipped to Phoenix, Arizona, to be kept in cold storage. Since then a growing number of people have followed his example, and chapters of the Cryonics Society have been formed in Los Angeles, Phoenix, and New York. No one holds out real promise that the bodies could ever be restored, but the thin hope causes a few to pay $4,500 for a capsule plus $50 a month to keep the bodies immersed in liquid nitrogen at 360° below zero.[18]

Not many people enjoy life or fear death enough to use such extreme measures to maintain intact the husk of dust to which nature intends us to return. The hope of being revived to new life, however, is based on more than a century of experimentation in using cold treatment of disease. Most such work has concentrated not on preservation but rather on destruction of unwanted tissue.

As early as 1851 James Arnott, a British surgeon, reported using a salt-ice mixture which produced temperatures down to 4° below zero to slow the development of certain cancers. Use of low temperature in surgery gained little headway, however, until technical advances in space-rocket propulsion provided a ready supply of liquefied gases, such as oxygen, nitrogen, and hydrogen, and safe techniques for containing and handling these super-cold fluids.

In 1961 a New York neurosurgeon, Irving S. Cooper, along with the Union Carbide Corporation, developed a practical cryosurgery unit in which liquid nitrogen was used as the freezing agent for local tissue destruction. The freezing agent, which can be controlled from zero down to more than 200° below zero, is inserted into the desired area by a needle probe.

Dr. Cooper demonstrated the technique on a patient suffering from brain tumor. He inserted the needle through a hole in the skull and positioned its point in the center of the tumor. Then, by injecting the super-cold liquid into the tumor, an ice ball was formed within and around it. This made it easier to remove the hardened mass from the surrounding brain tissue. Also the tumor may be left in place, since it is known the tissue will die after such treatment. As it thaws, the dead material is removed by the standard processes of blood circulation.

Destroying tissue in place is now widely used for removing many growths, shrinking diseased tonsils, prostate tissue, and many cancers. Cryosurgery works to destroy unwanted tissue by forming ice in the cells. This bursts the cell walls, causing them to die. Tissue is also destroyed by freeze-damaging the small blood vessels, and the cells die from lack of oxygen.

Cryosurgery offers major prospects for improved human health, but research has indicated that freezing tissue to certain temperatures at certain speed can permit rethawing the tissue *without* damage. It is this possibility that encourages those people who now seek the frozen-body route to immortality. If and when this technique is proved reliable, it may become possible for people to choose suspended animation by freezing *before* death. Such a choice would enhance the possibilities for revival and again offer hope that during years of frozen hibernation, medical science would have found the means to cure previously incurable diseases. Suspended animation, in one form or another, may become important in centuries ahead as a way for men to explore beyond the solar system in space voyages requiring dozens or hundreds of years.

Such possibilities, along with the grand illumination of the past decade into the human cell and its genetic code, promise a truly new age of human life. We stand at the threshold of a magnificent and terrifying experiment in which we will be able to remake ourselves and take over the course of our own evolution.

PART IV

The Perfection
of Man

CHAPTER 12

"Homo
Novus"

Dr. James D. Watson, Nobel Prize winner and codiscoverer of the DNA double helix, recently predicted that "within a year a scientist will conceive a baby in a test tube and successfully place it inside a woman who will bear the child.

"Then," he said, "all hell will break loose."

The distinguished scientist made this prediction in testimony before the House Science Subcommittee of Congress. The "hell" to which he referred is the political, social, and religious storm which will be stirred by conception and birth of the world's first "test tube" baby. It could happen by the time this book is published.

"The United States should take the lead now," he urged the subcommittee, "in forming an international commission to ask: 'Do we really want to do this?' and perhaps take steps to make it illegal."[1]

Watson's testimony offered sharp and somber emphasis to the explosive progress which biologists and biochemists have made in the past ten years in understanding—and manipu-lating—the innermost processes of the living cell which deter-mine the shape of our lives and the moment of our death.

The test-tube baby is only one of the dubious treasures that new knowledge is placing within our hands. We stand at the edge of an era in which human effort can control the perfection of man. That high optimism was expressed by Dr. Robert Sinsheimer, chairman of Cal Tech's Division of Biology:

> When the historians of what hopefully will be a more humane future look back at this, the twentieth century, one may wonder what they will consider worthy of note. Our recurrent wars? Our ideological and racial fanaticism?
>
> More likely they will recall this was the century in which man first left earth, or certainly the century in which man first kindled nuclear fire. And I feel sure they will recall that this was the century in which man first understood his inheritance and evolution, first saw clearly how he came to be. For the first time, a living creature understood his origin.
>
> We are the heirs of Icarus. We have become the latter-day Prometheus. But even in ancient myths men were men and gods were gods, and man could not rise above his nature to chart his destiny. But now we can confront that chance and choice and soon we shall have the power consciously to alter our inheritance, our very nature.[2]

It's a great promise, that of guiding our own destiny to the evolution of new man (*homo novus*?), but our hardest task may be finding a perfect definition for perfection. If we can remake ourselves, what kind of people should we be?

We are not forced to make the decision this week or next. Most of the promised wonders of genetic manipulation are some years away from full application, but it is time we began thinking about how to use the immense power which lies ahead.

"New information is being obtained in the field of biochemical genetics at an extremely rapid rate which will undoubtedly continue to increase within the foreseeable future," said Dr. Marshall W. Nirenberg, winner of the 1968 Nobel Prize in physiology and medicine. "Thus far this knowledge has had relatively little effect upon man because more information must be obtained before practical application will be possible.

"The technical problems that must be overcome are formidable. However, when these obstacles have been removed, this knowledge will greatly influence man's future. Such power can be used wisely or unwisely, for the betterment or detriment of mankind."

Three men advise us that vast social change lies ahead. Where do we stand today?

The genetic language is known, and it seems clear that most forms of life use the same language. Simple genetic "messages" can be man-made, chemically. Genetic surgery on microorganisms is a reality. Genes can be prepared from one strain of bacteria and inserted into another, which is then changed genetically.

What of the future?

Meaningful genetic messages will be synthesized chemically. Since the instructions will be written in the language that cells understand, the messages will be used to program cells. These, then, will carry out the new instructions, and the program may be inherited by succeeding generations.

"I don't know how long it will take before it will be possible to program cells with synthesized messages," Dr. Nirenberg said. "If a poll were taken of a dozen knowledgeable investigators, a dozen different answers probably would be obtained. My guess is that cells will be programmed with synthetic information within twenty-five years. If effort along these lines were intensified, bacteria might be programmed in five years."[3]

We do not yet know what genetic program we might devise to build the *perfect* man, but this fledgling art may first be put to work correcting obvious imperfections, genetic diseases, and possibly cancer. We have seen that many human deformities may be eliminated through genetic counseling which helps parents decide whether or not to have defective children. Even more beneficial will be the ability to alter the genes directly, but this is a tiny arena in which the biologists are working.

There are three thousand genes in a simple bacterium, and a

million in the cell of a human being. Until recently it was impossible to distinguish anything this small, but in 1970 three University of Chicago physicists, using a special electron microscope technique, obtained the first photographs of atoms (thorium and uranium), the units of which molecules are built. This method can measure an object four billionths of an inch in size. Albert V. Crewe, who headed the team, said it should enable biologists to measure the precise shapes of certain molecules and calculate speeds of chemical reactions. It may be possible to read off the genetic code along a strand of DNA chromosome.[4]

Developments toward insertion of new information into the infinitesimal tape recorders of life have multiplied. Two researchers at the University of Hawaii "persuaded" the protein-making machinery of bacteria to make rabbit protein under direction of a strand of rabbit messenger RNA.[5] Professor Jonathan Beckwith, of Harvard University, reported isolation of a pure gene from the *e. coli* bacterium. Dr. Max Birnstiel at Edinburgh University claimed that two years earlier he had isolated a pure frog gene.[6]

The first *synthetic* gene was created in 1970 by Dr. Khorana, as previously noted. At the University of Chicago Dr. Arnold W. Ravin said his team had affected the lives of unborn bacteria by injecting cell cultures with genetic material taken from other bacteria that had mutated to resist antibiotics. Microbes grown from these injected cultures had developed the same resistance, indicating that the inserted genetic material had become a functioning part of the organism's DNA. Such studies could lead to the correction of genetic defects and cellular malfunction involved in diseases such as cancer and diabetes.

"With few exceptions, attempts to produce this transformation in higher organisms have not succeeded," Dr. Ravin said. "We think the possibility exists, but we simply haven't found the right conditions under which transformations can occur."[7]

The possibility of gene transfer in higher organisms became

reality soon after. In England Professor Henry Harris at Oxford University extracted a gene from the red blood cells of a chicken and inserted it into a mouse cell. This enabled the mouse cells (in laboratory culture) to manufacture a previously missing enzyme known as IAP. With genetic information from the chick cells, the mouse cells proceeded to grow and manufacture IAP. When this gene is absent in humans, it causes the Lesch-Nyhan syndrome, a childhood disease causing early death.

The connection between chickens, mice, and men may seem remote, but not in the chain of work Professor Harris is following. He reported success also in transferring genes from mouse to hamster cells and from toad to mouse cells. Now he is attempting to transfer genetic material from chicken cells to human cells. In theory cells that have had their genetic defect repaired could be grown in quantity in the test tube, then be injected back into a patient to repair the defect and enable him to make his own enzyme.[8]

Until recently the human cell had resisted the art of microsurgeons, but researchers also scored a breakthrough on that front in 1970. A team at the Sloan-Kettering Institute for Cancer Research in New York reported they were able to free chromosomes from cells by injecting silicone oil. The chromosome pairs were then picked out and injected directly into other cells. The three performing this infinitely small operation were Elaine Diacumakos, Scott Holland, and Pauline Pecora. They found that the human cells survived the operation. They even managed to introduce virus fractions into the nuclei of cancer cells without killing them.

"This ability to damage the structure of human cells specifically, and to transplant components from one cell to another, could prove of great value in discovering how both normal and cancerous human cells tick," the microsurgeons wrote. Their equipment included instruments equipped with micro-positioners for holding cells in place, four micro-injection units, and a conventional microscope. The genetic "engineering" was performed in a chamber filled with the cell medium and sealed with oil to maintain sterility. The three said they had operated on about two thousand individual cells.[9]

Surgery at this microscopic level seems unbelievable to the layman, and the work has been done only with cell cultures outside the living organism. Such techniques, however, lead toward the primary goal of injecting new "healthy" information into cells and organisms suffering genetic disease or cancer and thus reversing the pathological condition. It may be possible someday to remove a specific faulty gene from a single germ cell, replace the gene with a good one, and use the egg or sperm to form a new creature free of fault. The laser beam, which can be focused to a point down to 1/10,000 of an inch, may become a major tool in this sort of operation.

One of the most promising methods for accomplishing this work involves the virus, which we normally dread. As previously shown, many viruses contain the ability to "bore" into a cell and override the genetic information on the cell's DNA. Utilizing this natural action, biologists expect to impress a "proper" gene into the viral apparatus, then let the virus carry it into place in the human cell. This offers hope for curing or preventing many of the genetic ills and degenerative diseases of man.

One aspect of manipulating and changing components in the cell is the possibility of making entirely new forms of life. This work has been supported by the National Aeronautics and Space Administration. The idea is that someday we might design creatures capable of living on other planets, sent on ahead to help make new worlds more livable before man arrives. A plant that could take root on Mars and enrich the oxygen atmosphere, for example, might help to make that planet more hospitable by the next century when we run out of living space on earth.

The notion that first terrestrial life may have been "planted" by some outside agency has been around for a long time, but the thought that *we* might plant life elsewhere bears the aura of godliness. Short of that exalted state is the work of James F. Danielli and associates at the State University of New York in Buffalo. They achieved the first artificial synthesis of a living cell. Danielli, with Joan Lorch and Kwang W. Heon, did *not* create life from raw materials, but rather reassembled parts of three different amoebas into one functional new cell.

As Danielli describes it, the team removed the nucleus of one amoeba with a microprobe and sucked out most of the cell's cytoplasm with a tiny pipette. Then they inserted into the remaining membrane a nucleus and cytoplasm which had been removed from other cells. The operation has been done many times. In 70 percent of their efforts, using amoebas of the same strain, the new cells were alive and continued to reproduce with their new structure. When it was tried with different strains, however, success was achieved only twice in 434 tries.

With continued experimentation Danielli believes it will be possible to produce amoebas with totally new characteristics, a possibility that "opens up a new era of artificial life synthesis." Some of the new earthly life forms he can visualize include rice or wheat with nitrogen-fixation genes transplanted from blue-green algae, tailor-made microorganisms for high-speed digestion of sewage, and a creature that would need only sunlight to desalt seawater. Danielli agreed it might even be possible, by cell transplantation, to cross a man with a horse, "though I can't see any reason for doing it, mind you." As he builds new organisms out of old, he is highly conscious of the possibility of creating a virus or other microbe that might be harmful. "All care must be taken," he said, "to discover any undesirable or harmful new properties appearing in such synthesized organisms, and to determine what effect they will have on existing ecological conditions before introducing these organisms to the environment at large."[10]

Creating new life forms is one phase of the game. Another is replacement of defective genes with right-thinking ones. A third, and most intriguing, possibility lies in the fact that every cell of the body contains the information needed to build *all* of the body, though most cells build only a special part and then stop. This faculty of differentiation and "knowing" when to start and stop has spawned its own special school of cell research known as developmental biology.

"Our immediate goal," said Professor Aron A. Moscona at the University of Chicago, "is to discover how different cell types—liver, brain, muscle, kidney—arise from the parent cell, the egg. We also must know how cells become organized into orderly tissues and organs. What are the processes, the time table, and the blueprints that guide embryonic cells in making an organism, and why do they sometimes fail (as in cancer)?"[11]

In the specialized cells of higher creatures at least 90 percent of the DNA is repressed or turned off because only a fraction of its total message is needed to make that particular organ. Also certain molecules, such as hormones, can turn on a gene again once it has done its job and has been turned off. The question is how to activate the genetic material selectively to do things we might want it to do.

John Gurdon at Oxford University experimented with the South African clawed toad. He took cells from the lining of the intestine, which have no continuing function except to make digestive enzymes, and removed the nucleus. Then he removed the nucleus of a toad egg and replaced it with the nucleus from the intestinal cells. The egg cell, with the intestinal nucleus, then proceeded to develop into a tadpole and a full-grown toad.

"All the genetic information about how to go through the whole developmental and reproductive cycle of an adult animal is contained in the specialized body cell," explained Dr. James Bonner at Cal Tech. "Since in an adult organism there are many different kinds of specialized cells—and each contains all of the genes for making the whole organism—it is apparent that in a given kind of specialized cell most of the genes must be turned off, inert, not making their gene product."

Bonner used the potato as an example of how an environmental change can reactivate genes to go to work again. When the potato is lying in the bin, the cells essentially have all their genes turned off. But if a piece is sliced off, the cells at the exposed edge get busy and start dividing, trying to make a new skin. The end of the sliced potato turns brown.

"We can see now that the cells in the developing organism are continuously monitoring their environment and seeing what kinds of things are out there," Bonner said. "Then they turn on the right genes to develop into the kind of cell appropriate to that environment." An analogy is found in the human liver, which regenerates its mass if part of it is removed.

"We know that many lower organisms have embryonic cells left at the base of the limbs which, if a limb is cut off, can regenerate a whole new limb or a whole new organ. By the same token, we now know how to take a cell—as in the case of the toad or potato—and change its stance of gene activity to make it think it is a fertilized egg.

"So in the future," Bonner said, "we should be able to take a single cell and reset the genetic program to any desired point to make that cell or group of cells turn into a new organ, a replacement organ or a new liver. Maybe you will go to the doctor and he will say: 'Well, I think your heart isn't so good now. Maybe we had better start growing you a new one, and in two or three years it will be grown up and we can plumb it in.' I would hope one day we would be able to regenerate organs and tissues."[12]

Out of dark antiquity we have climbed many ladders of knowledge. We have learned to cure men with drugs and repair with surgery. We have made artificial parts and transplanted vital organs. We see ways now which may cleanse civilization of its genetic defects. Finally we visualize the artifice by which the aging body may regenerate its own dying organs and eventually erase degenerative disease. Perhaps immortality is really within our reach—if we want it.

Extending or improving lives of the sick and aged, however, is only the smaller part of what is promised by the new age of biology. Greater changes are possible at the beginning of life with the anticipated new tools of cell engineering. Here is what the geneticists themselves say is within reach:

1. Fertile women who do not want the burden of child-bearing may have other women bear their children for them.

2. Infertile women can bear their own children by implant.

3. The sex of the embryo can be controlled so that parents may choose whether they're to have a boy or a girl.

4. Children may be reproduced *outside* the human womb.

5. And—most staggering of all—we may produce limitless numbers of duplicate embryos, called clones. This would make possible the exact copying of anyone—such as 10,000 Picassos, 100 Einsteins, 1,000 Neil Armstrongs, 10,000 Elizabeth Taylors, or 100,000 Hitlers.[13]

The prospects are wonderful for making a new race of men, terrifying in their potential for making the wrong men. This part of it, the new breed, began with artificial insemination.

Any technique that tampers with nature's way of doing things or with standard social practice, particularly in matters of sexual reproduction, is vaguely distasteful, sometimes frightening, and always slow to be accepted. The production of fine food animals to feed an increasing population has been accomplished during the past quarter century, however, by the ability to take seed from a prize bull and impregnate perhaps a thousand cows by artificial means. This is standard practice in animal and plant genetics. It enhances nature's capability to produce something we want, and we are not concerned about disturbing the sexual habits of domestic animals.

Sexual habits of people are another matter, evoking emotional overtones of love, marriage, and parenthood. Despite questions involved in legitimacy and inheritance, artificial insemination has become accepted for human reproduction in many parts of the United States. Most people today worry about having too many children and contributing to the population explosion, but other couples wish desperately for children. Many women bear children by artificial insemination with sperm from anonymous donors, men whose pedigrees have been carefully checked for good mental, physical, and hereditary factors. Some ten thousand children are born each year from such conceptions in this country.[14]

Doctors are cautious about recommending artificial insemination from an outside donor because of the impact on the husband's pride and the question that might arise concerning legal parentage. These problems are not severe if thoroughly rationalized by husband and wife before taking the step.

Couples who now have children in this way never know the identity of the man who donated the sperm. The next step is to make a deliberate choice of the proxy father. This can be done when scientists perfect a system of sperm banks and when society is ready for it. Odds are that sperm banks will be ready first.

In 1969 Dr. Georg Sillo-Seidel, of Frankfurt, Germany, reported that a woman under his care had given birth to a child conceived from frozen sperm. The woman had been childless for five years, partially because her husband's job kept him away from home most of the time. The husband, thirty-three, donated sperm, which was then kept frozen by Dr. Sillo-Seidel until the most favorable moment for inseminating the wife. The doctor said the child was normal in every respect.

"The frozen sperm method," he said, "offers itself not only for cases in which the husband is prevented from being present at the time of ovulation, but also gives the possibility of concentrating semen or collecting it over a period of time."[15] Some doctors are now using the sperm bank to ensure the fertilization of women whose husbands have a low sperm count. In this case sperm may be accumulated and stored over a period of time until sufficient seed is available for impregnation. Many childless couples are helped to have children in this way.

The German birth may have been the first child to originate from germ cells preserved by cold, but the technique is not entirely new. It was learned some years ago that male sperm (though not female eggs) can be treated with glycerol, which enables the germ cells to survive storage at 196° below zero. Sperm from pedigreed bulls thus can continue to sire offspring years after their earthly remains have become rump steak.

In like fashion, sperm collected from exceptional men in society can be preserved to maintain the seed of strong genetic specimens (genotypes) for reproduction in years to come. From such a sperm bank a couple might select the seed of an athlete, scientist, or scholar to father their child. The offspring, due to differences in environment and education, would not duplicate the original through a lifetime, but such seed would guarantee a head start. President Nixon and hundreds of other Americans already have samples of their sperm preserved in refrigerated chambers awaiting the day of their second coming.[16] The time, then, is not far removed when a woman might walk into a frozen-sperm bank (or make a selection from a list) and choose a John Glenn or a Jonas Salk or a Nixon—or even one of the Beatles—to father her child, though that father would never know it or might even be dead.

The sperm bank will solve the problem of fertility for couples in which the husband is sterile or away at the wrong time, but what about the woman who is infertile or wants a child without the discomfort of bearing it herself? That problem is also on the threshold of solution by a trail which also leads back to established practices in animal genetics.

Not long ago Dr. E. S. E. Havez, experimental biologist at Wayne State University, asked a colleague in Germany to send him one hundred head of prize sheep. The friend complied by airmailing Dr. Havez a box which could be held in one hand. Inside was a female rabbit with one hundred potential rams and ewes, all tiny embryos, nestled alive inside her womb. Upon arrival the embryos were removed and each planted within the uterus of a ewe. Months later one hundred lambs were born while their real mother and father grazed contentedly on a mountainside in Germany.[17]

We are not yet ready to start shipping human embryos by

rabbit, but the age of the so-called test-tube baby has already dawned. As early as the 1940's Dr. John Rock, the Harvard University birth-control pioneer, succeeded in fertilizing a female egg with sperm outside the human body—in a test tube. The new cells died shortly thereafter, but *in vitro* (in glass) fertilization had been demonstrated. In the 1950's Dr. Rock's pioneering work was followed by several researchers, including Dr. Landrum B. Shettles, professor of obstetrics and gynecology at Columbia University.[18]

While performing surgery on women, Dr. Shettles pierced the ovaries of his patients and drew some of their eggs up into a syringe. Then he drew off some of the follicular fluid and other internal "equipment" which permits an egg to ripen, develop, and receive the male sperm within the genetic apparatus. From all of this he formed the culture medium in which the removed eggs could mature and undergo fertilization. When an egg was ready, Dr. Shettles placed it in a sterile dish containing another culture medium necessary for life and then added millions of sperm cells, which were permitted to fight their way to the egg, just as in nature.

Dr. Shettles became the first man to witness the drama of human fertilization. He watched the ovum as it was accosted by thousands of sperm cells. The dance of love continued for hours before one sperm cell finally penetrated the egg, merged with the nucleus, and began growing a new being. In 1971 Dr. Shettles and Dr. Daniele Petrucci, of Bologna, Italy, reported they had kept fertilized eggs (zygotes) alive and growing for six days, the time at which the embryo normally would attach itself within the lining of the mother's uterus. Dr. Petrucci kept at least one egg living and growing in the test tube for nearly two months.[19] Dr. Robert C. Edwards, of Cambridge University, and his associate Patrick C. Steptoe also announced they had grown embryos to the one-hundred-cell blastocyst stage, ready for planting within the womb.

The next step is doing the first live transplant, and this has probably already been tried by Dr. Edwards, Dr. Shettles, or perhaps others. If such an experiment is successful (nine months of waiting is still necessary), we may very soon hear of the first child who began life in a test tube. If unsuccessful, it will have been aborted. Sooner or later the experiment will succeed, and as Dr. Watson told Congress, all hell will break loose. "With the laboratory growth of human embryos," he said, "the nature of the bond between parents and their children and everyone's values about their individual uniqueness could be changed beyond recognition."[20]

Many things will become possible with this biological breakthrough, not the least of which is a woman's freedom to choose how to have children and which children to have. If a woman is sterile for reasons other than egg production, her doctor may remove an egg by surgery, combine it with her husband's seed, and then plant the embryo back in her womb for normal growth. If a woman wants a child but not pregnancy, she and her husband could donate egg and sperm, which could be mated in the test tube and planted in another woman willing (or hired) to bear the child. Finally, if there were another man and woman the husband and wife admired more than themselves, the wife could grow a baby born from someone else's egg and sperm. A single woman could do the same.

Dr. Havez at Wayne State believes that within ten to twenty years a woman may choose her offspring routinely by prenatal adoption. She might walk into an embryo bank, look down a row of packets, and select her baby label. Each packet would contain a frozen embryo, and each label would identify qualities such as mind, disposition, character, and physical fitness of the egg and sperm donors. The embryo could then be thawed and planted in her womb to mature to birth.[21] One advantage to birth by embryo implant is that it would give doctors the opportunity to detect abnormalities before the actual pregnancy begins. Also, by amniocentesis, this study could continue during the early months of pregnancy, permitting an abortion in case there should arise signs of genetic defect or deficiency.

Dr. Ernest Beutler, of the City of Hope Medical Center in Los Angeles, believes that test-tube babies will be a technical reality in fifty to one hundred years but will never be widely used as a means of reproduction. "Apart from the technical aspects which make it hard to do on a large scale," he said, "I think women psychologically will want to bear their own babies."[22]

Another impending benefit of the genetic revolution will permit parents to select the sex of their child, even if they have it by old-fashioned sexual intercourse.

For some reasons, perhaps because of the need for farmhands and soldiers, or the more prideful desire to continue the masculine name and bloodline, boy babies have always been more welcome than girl babies. The Jewish Talmud says, "When a girl is born, the walls are crying." In the Koran it is written: "When an Arab hears a daughter has been born to him, his face becomes saddened." Ancient Romans were taxed more for girls than for boys. Repugnant as these thoughts may be for today's liberated women, people of all lands traditionally have attempted to predict a child's sex before birth and to conceive the sex of their wishes.

European peasants believed that when both breasts of a pregnant woman look healthy, swell equally, and harden at the same time, this is a sign of a male child. Hippocrates believed that begetting male children is more certain if the phallus is inserted as deeply as possible during coitus. In Italy, if a boy is wanted, the husband bites his wife's ear during intercourse. (There is no record of what this has produced other than sore ears.)[23] Needless to say, most of these beliefs are as groundless as spitting into the wind on a night of the full moon, and even the wisest obstetricians have an uncertain batting average predicting the sex of unborn children.

We have seen that tapping the amniotic fluid of a pregnant woman can give definite evidence of the child's sex, but soon it will be possible to *choose* the sex, through artificial insemination, before fertilization. It has been determined that a child's sex is decided by different spermatozoa and eggs. One test shows that the Y chromosome (which promises a boy) fluoresces and becomes visible under certain light. By phase-contrast microscopy it has also been learned that "female" sperm have elongated oval-shaped heads, while the "males" have compact round heads. Male sperm also appear to be smaller than the sperm that will create a female. This offers the prospect that the sperm can be separated and then only the desired sex introduced to the egg at spawning time.[24]

Aside from allowing parents to choose a boy or girl as they wish, this faculty will be important in eliminating many genetic diseases and defects. Most of these, including hemophilia, occur most commonly in boys. So the old trend to keep "trying for a boy" may finally give way to a preference for girls. The ability to choose the sex of children with 90 percent reliability is expected by 1980.[25] The way biological discoveries have leapfrogged predictions in recent years, it may happen sooner.

Among other discoveries is a family of so-called fertility drugs which help previously barren women to have children. One of these is a natural extract, the pituitary hormone gonadotrophin, which can induce ovulation. In an unusual number of cases use of fertility drugs has led to multiple births of identical children, and this seems especially likely when a woman has become pregnant after she stopped using hormone preparations to prevent conception.

One case involved a thirty-two-year-old British woman who had been barren for eight years because of failure to ovulate. Doctors administered gonadotrophin, and she became pregnant. Early in her pregnancy doctors were able to predict, by ultrasonic examination, that she was carrying quintuplets. She entered Queen Charlotte's Hospital in London during her thirty-first week of pregnancy, and five babies were born by cesarean section. All thrived.[26]

In 1971 Dr. Gennaro Montanini in Rome removed fifteen perfectly formed fetuses from the womb of a thirty-five-year-old housewife who had been undergoing fertility treatment.

The ten girls and five boys had smothered in the womb, but it was believed to be the largest single pregnancy in medical history.[27] Such multiple births forecast the day when it will be possible to produce identical copies of any human being in any number.

That idea originated with plant genetics. In 1902 the Austrian botanist Gottlieb Haberlandt predicted it should be possible to raise whole plants from single cells. Sixty years later Professor F. C. Steward, of Cornell University, did it. He grew thousands of tiny carrot plantlets from single carrot root cells. Each was identical to the plant from which it came. Later, as we have seen, John Gurdon, of Oxford, did the same thing with the South African clawed toad by transplanting cell nuclei. The same may be possible with people, some think by the year 2000.[28] A woman might then be able to give birth to an identical copy of herself. This is cloning.

"All we have to do is take the nucleus from a body cell," explained Dr. Bonner, "and implant it into the egg which has been enucleated and we can develop a new adult organism with the genetic constitution of the donor of the body cell. There is nothing to prevent us from taking two body cells from that same donor and growing two identical twins of the donor.

"As a matter of fact," he added, "there is nothing to prevent us from taking a thousand. We could grow any desired number of genetically identical people from individuals who have desirable characteristics. They won't have the learning and wisdom of the donor. Those things must be acquired."

The power to make unlimited identical people arouses amazement and doubt of the wisdom of doing it. Dr. Bonner tells of the letter he received from a young girl in New Delhi, India. "I don't understand why you have to go and invent a new way of making people," she wrote. "If your way of making people works, be sure and don't send any of them to India."

"When the time comes that we pursue these policies," Bonner said, "I think that we will have, indeed, a new super species of human being. It really appears to be within our power—if not today, then in the very near future—to cause our species to develop along any lines which we deem desirable."[29]

Biological science conceivably could do away with normal sexual reproduction entirely. Dr. Robert Goodlin at Stanford University (and he is not the only one) has a steel chamber in which he can gestate and watch the growth of tiny human embryos. The device is much like a heart-lung machine. The umbilical cord passes through a coiled cellulose tube that bathes the embryo in fluid and oxygen, keeping it alive for forty-eight hours and more. Scientists think it will take five more years to understand how gases are exchanged between the fetus and its environment, with ten years more to understand the transfer of liquids and solids.

Then the true test-tube baby may be born, without intervention of a mother's womb. Aldous Huxley, in his *Brave New World*, placed the fictional baby factory several centuries in the future. We may see it by the end of this century.

That leaves two more steps of predictable magic to come from the biological arts. One is to create entirely new chromosomal patterns for human beings—making people such as have never existed before or shaping them to the highest examples known in society. Scientists eventually may be able to plant new human traits, such as the ability to resist damaging radiation or environmental pollution.

The second step, as in Dr. Danielli's amoebas, might cross people with animals for whatever purpose might be imagined. Then at last we would see the chimera of ancient mythology, which is not exactly a happy thought. The original chimera was supposed to have been a fire-breathing she monster with a lion's head, a goat's body, and the tail of a dragon or serpent.

Such experiments may be left to a new-day Dr. Frankenstein, but elsewhere the tools are near at hand to achieve the perfection of man and create *homo novus*.

Now who on earth is qualified to define perfection?

CHAPTER 13

Serpent
in Paradise

"This is an old story, one that links Prometheus to Adam. Once man knows that he can know, and that he can judge good and evil, his acts have a moral significance whether he chooses to learn or to deny."[1]

Those words by Joshua Lederberg, Stanford Nobel laureate, lend a Delphic summation to the overall problem. The serpent is always in paradise, always offering the apple of knowledge. Humans are always naïve children, reaching above their grasp, seeking out dark trees of forbidden fruit often without the wisdom to eat and digest it. Once the apple is eaten, no matter how marvelous its benefits, we must accept the terrible responsibility that goes with it.

Dr. Margaret Mead, the noted anthropologist, accused genetic engineers of "playing God." "Any manipulation of the population puts a terrific moral responsibility on human beings. It's human beings playing God and that's a dangerous thing to do."[2]

In Rome the Vatican's official spokesman greeted experiments with fertilizing human eggs in the test tube by branding them "immoral acts and absolutely illicit."[3]

Barry Goldwater, onetime candidate for the U.S. Presidency, warned: "Should such genetic engineering take place under federal sponsorship, there is at least the possibility that control of the processes also would be by federal authority. . . . To give bureaucrats such power would be to give them the power to mold populations to their blueprints."[4]

These are only first sparks of an inferno soon to be kindled. Politicians and others of power either do not comprehend what the biological artists tell us is possible, or else they are so overwhelmed by the potential that they do not know which way to turn. Full awareness is not yet upon us, but the ability to remake human beings to our own design will disturb the roots of almost every concept we have held to be true by evolutionary distillation of the ages. Physical, mental, moral, ethical, social, and religious "truths" will be severely wrenched into new shape as we practice what Lederberg terms *orthobiosis*, the correction or perfection of life and of man.

The first, and greatest, question is whether or not to allow practice of the new magic.

Shall we permit women to choose fathers of their children, wed or unwed, of known or unknown identity? Shall we store the seed of great men to fertilize future generations?

Shall we erase genetic defects by abortion or by prohibiting certain people from having children?

Shall we allow people to live unlimited time, overcrowding the world still more? Shall we make a hundred or a million Xerox copies of a man or woman, and, if so, which ones should we copy?

Shall we permit scientists with computers to build new chromosomal patterns and change the shape of men forever? Shall we devise entirely new creatures and perhaps cross them with men to obtain special talents, such as small size and the ability to survive travel between the stars?

These are more difficult questions than the human race has faced before. They are not limited to America or any single nation. Scientists of all the world have access to the same information. Thus if there are to be sanctions or prohibitions upon any phase of biological engineering, they must be worldwide. A democratic nation might pass a law against cloning, but how would it coexist with a militant nation whose leaders elected to fashion a million super-soldiers? And since it is so difficult for the politicians and diplomats to agree on the relatively simple problem of banning war, how can we hope to achieve a consensus on issues that strike at the root of human nature as well as life and death?

The scientists who make the discoveries must come to our aid because they alone can completely comprehend the biological revolution, predict its timing, and list alternatives clearly enough for the rest of us to make decisions. Those decisions must be made by all the people. There can be no Big Brother, at the head of government, scientific community, or church, passing judgment on the pros and cons in secret, convinced he is doing the right thing for all of us. Too often we have learned belatedly that affairs of state conducted in secret proved in the long run to be tragically wrong. We cannot afford to be wrong in remaking men because the result will rule our children and their children's children. It is no longer enough for a brilliant man to say: "Look at this new thing I have found. Use it as you wish." Now this brilliant man must teach us as well.

Among the explosions of new technology in this century, the unleashing of nuclear energy stands out as the pivotal point separating the old age of science from the new. Burgeoning from a mathematical formula out of the brain of Albert Einstein, scientists and engineers developed the power to destroy the world. This cast a spell of guilt over many who saw the results of their labor in the ruins of Hiroshima and Nagasaki. Some campaigned politically against proliferation of the bomb. Some still seek to throttle the inevitable and beneficial use of nuclear power because of possible harm from nuclear radiation. The bomb also widened a schism between technical innovation and lagging society unable to absorb the pace of new discoveries. From an object of comic-strip ridicule, the "mad" scientist became a figure vaguely feared and regarded with superstitious awe by those who could not comprehend his work. What violent surprise might we anticipate next?

As a result, biological scientists who see the direction their work is taking are sometimes reluctant to reveal it. This tendency, in relation to Dr. Khorana's synthesis of an artificial gene, was noted by Victor K. McElheny writing in *Technology Review* at Massachusetts Institute of Technology:

> It is simply foolish for morally-concerned molecular biologists to seek absolution in advance of any role in building some sort of biological time bomb. A certain sourness, a sort of facile desperation, has overspread much recent discussion of advances in fundamental science, including Khorana's feat. It is as if new knowledge about nature brought an expansion of danger instead of converting inchoate, shapeless anxieties into graspable, definable problems.
>
> Such emotion is as irrelevant as it ever was to the tasks of civilization. The discoveries that poets and scientists make are always there. Men may shrink from them, but the tasks do not go away. They make a pathway into the times ahead and may be the strongest pressure upon us to assure that human beings will be alive at that time.[5]

It's a logical argument. All knowledge of the universe exists; why apologize if we happen to discover a piece of it? The position of today's scientist was clarified by Dr. Nirenberg at the National Institutes of Health:

> Most biochemical geneticists work because the search for knowledge is an exciting creative adventure—much as an artist's or poet's exploration is creative. His primary aim is not that of creating powerful tools for society. However, this cumulative accretion of knowledge does create such tools: thus the scientist has a responsibility which an eminent virologist, Salvadore Luria, stated eloquently:
>
>> The impact of science on human affairs [Luria wrote] imposes on its practitioners an inescapable responsibility. It creates the urge to seek useful applications and to foster

their general acceptance. On the other hand, it may restrain the scientist from pursuing a line of research that is clearly leading to evil applications. Yet the progress of science is so rapid, almost catastrophic, that it creates an imbalance between the power it places in the hands of man and the social conditions in which this power is exerted.

The scientist should cultivate his own alertness to developments that may suddenly add new powers to man. The scientific habits of skepticism and restraint, of curbing fantasy and distrusting fancy, inhibit the scientist's effort to speculate on what the future may bring. He must, however, prepare the public to cope with the foreseeable consequences of advances which he anticipates.[6]

Prolongation of life, control of fertility and population, treatment and prevention of anxiety and aggressiveness, the enhancement of memory, intelligence, and pleasure—all of these exotic things wait ahead of us, but can we afford to try them?

"We need only consult Huxley's *Brave New World* to get an indication of where we are likely to be going," said Leon Kass, of the National Academy of Science Committee on Life Sciences and Social Policy. "In Huxley we encounter a society dedicated to homogeneity and stability, administered by instant gratifications, and peopled by creatures of human shape but of stunted humanity. They consume, fornicate, take 'soma,' and operate the machinery that makes it all possible. They do not read, write, think, love, or govern themselves. Creativity and curiosity, reason and passion, exist only in a rudimentary and mutilated form. In short, they are not men at all."

Kass fears the same for us if the large decisions on the use of advances in biomedical technology are made "technocratically and self-servingly. The family is rapidly becoming the only institution in an increasingly impersonal world where each person is loved not for what he does or makes, but simply because he is," he said. "Can our humanity survive the family's destruction?"[7]

Other scientists harbor similar fears. "The day of genetic engineering or modification of development is on the horizon," said Dr. Moscona at the University of Chicago. "Our moral and scientific attitude must be based on knowledge of facts and issues."[8]

Young scientists working with Professor Beckwith at Harvard in isolating genes from bacteria stated concern that their work will "loose more evil than good. You could phase everybody into the same sort of skin color, height, personality, making it appear as an aid to humanity," said Lawrence Eron. "This is a much more subtle way to do things than killing, which we all recognize as overtly wrong."[9]

Dr. Danielli, both applauded and criticized for his experiments in synthesizing new creatures, identified part of the problem. "The trouble is that although vast sums of money are spent in science and technology in developing the research, only trivial amounts are spent on trying to predict the results of the work on society," he said.[10]

"How do you judge when what is the optimum genotype in one set of circumstances may be inferior in another?" asked Dr. Glass, of New York University. "If we knew how to define the goal of a 'good race,' we might breed for it as we do animals; but the lesson seems clear. In selecting for certain characteristics in their animal breeds, the breeders seem always to sacrifice other desirable traits.

"The human races are not animal breeds, but each has been tested out by selection in a natural environment. Probably each is superior in its own way. We are living in a world where travel and migration have vastly increased the intermixture of the genes. The North American Negro's genes already are about 30 percent derived from white ancestry; yet past rates of intermixing will require something like two thousand years before an eventual equilibrium is reached and individual genetic differences are no longer noticeably 'racial.' Would it be a good thing to speed up this rate of intermixture? By controlled reproduction it could be done, but what would the social consequences be? The control of human behavior by artificial means will have become by the year 2000 a frightening possibility."

Dr. Glass pointed out that government—Big Brother—might use tranquilizers or hallucinogens like LSD to keep the population from becoming unruly or overly independent. More subtle forms of conditioning would lead people to react in predictable ways, desired by government or by commercial interests, without knowing that they were hoodwinked. The possibilities of controlled reproduction, Dr. Glass added, make these psychological methods of control even more drastic. "Here is our *Brave New World* in full, with bottled babies in different kinds of solutions that condition their mental growth to suit a certain caste."

He also questioned what disturbing effects will alter society and the family if all sexual life is liberated from relationship to reproduction. What will be the psychological consequences of a population with no personal ties either to the older generation or to the younger generation? Can we look forward to the brotherhood of mankind when there are no more parents, brothers, or children—only *people?*

"If we are going to develop a civilization broadly and soundly based upon scientific foundations—and we can hardly escape that now—every citizen, every man in the street, must learn what science truly is and what risks and quandaries, as well as what magnificent gifts, the powers that grow out of scientific discovery engender. Surely," Dr. Glass concluded, "that is our primary task."[11]

A sober solution to the problems posed by the biological revolution was the goal of Dr. Lederberg, of Stanford, when he asked Congress in 1970 to back a genetics task force to correlate new discoveries and channel research in right directions. He also defended against critics who argue that research should be stopped before it goes too far.

Lederberg pointed out that foreseeable tools are only extensions of the things men have done in the past to improve and extend their lives. The correction and perfection of life and of man, the meaning of his word *orthobiosis*, are already implemented on a large scale—constructively in the practice of medicine and hygiene, negatively via a global system that ensures that millions of underprivileged children will be mentally retarded by malnutrition and virus infection. Dr. Lederberg said:

> Applied genetics is so laden with religious implications about the nature of man that some question the morality of even investigating the scientific bases of humanity, just as others question the basic commitment of western culture to scientific inquiry. This was once called the work of the devil. The counterculture today denounces science simultaneously as a toy of the intellectuals and a tool of class oppression. Since Galileo the Establishment also has feared the revolutional impact of objective scientific inquiry on the mythologies which sustain the status quo.

Lederberg pointed out that man is the *historical* animal because his evolution is more a function of traditions and social forms than biological functions, but

> in the rapture of self-exaltation, many humanisms may nevertheless forget that evolution is a continuing process.
> The perfectability of man and the corollary of his present imperfection should stand out as one of the most precise implications of the evolutionary outlook. We should be optimistic and humble that our posterity will progress beyond our capabilities, even for moral judgment, to the same degree as our own proudly proclaimed emergence from apedom. We have one precept about values—that we ought to guarantee that there will be a posterity. . . . This supports the policy that the State must not intrude in the intimate lives of citizens except for the most inescapable needs of public order. This principal must be renewed and reinforced to stem the temptations of totalitarian exploitation of biological engineering.

The scientist expressed confidence that when the new tools of biology are perfected, society will control them with rational laws.

> The community will properly set bounds on the characteristics of individuals produced by any kind of rational design.

If the technical power now existed, the community probably would vent its wrath on any person who, for example, intentionally and knowingly produced an idiot. Laws for compulsory sterilization have wisely been held in abeyance mainly out of scientific uncertainties and the difficulties of fair enforcement. The same principles undoubtedly will evolve in our adjustment to genetic innovations.

The suppression of knowledge appears to me unthinkable, not only on ideological, but on merely logical grounds. How can the ignorant know what they should not know?[12]

Controversy regarding the application of genetic engineering and behavior control continued to boil through 1972, at least within the halls of science. Dr. Sinsheimer at Cal Tech proposed an international authority for genetic research as a safeguard against abuses of human modification for nationalistic purposes. Speaking at a conference sponsored by the Institute of Society, Ethics and the Life Sciences, he repeated emphatically that man is at a juncture in his own evolution.

"We have really only two choices," he said, "to proceed with all the wisdom we can develop, or to stagnate in fear and in doubt. The choice seems to me to be, are we as a species to lead a furtive, timorous existence, or do we seek to find the way to a higher state?"[13]

Karl H. Pribram, professor of psychiatry and psychology at Stanford, declared that the country needs a biological Bill of Rights adding the Constitutional "right to the pursuit of humanity." Only the guarantee of such rights, rather than changing man's brain and body through technology or drugs, he said, will "handle the current crisis of control in the affairs of man."[14]

Although most scientists urge control without stifling the advance of science, others believe the severity of potential problems has been overstated, or at least stated ahead of the proper time. One who holds this position is Dr. Herbert Stern, chairman of biology at the University of San Diego.

"They are uncertain what will be the results of the experiments they do in the lab," he said. "If they were certain of the outcome, there would be no need to do the experiments. So how can they possibly be so confident about things on a cosmic scale?"[15]

Francis Crick, codiscoverer of the DNA double helix, is confident that basic morals and common sense will prevail. Some of the wilder genetic proposals will never be adopted, he thinks, because "people will simply not stand for them."

Other opinions rattle off the pins of opposite extremes. The Roman Catholic Church warns that man must not tinker with such sacred values as life and the family for fear of disturbing the natural order of things. Philosopher Teilhard de Chardin writes of the coming scientific age when men will exult in "fathoming everything, trying everything, extending everything on their road to an ultimate Omega Point of shared Godhood."[16] Indeed, how could we hope to approach that godhood, which is so evidently our goal, without trying everything?

Joseph Fletcher, professor of medical ethics at the University of Virginia, says he favors virgin birth by genetic engineering if it accomplishes the greatest good for the greatest number. "It seems to me that laboratory reproduction is more 'human' than conception by ordinary heterosexual intercourse," he said. "I cannot see how either humanity or morality is served by genetic roulette [the present method of reproducing our species]." As for cloning, the vegetative reproduction of identical people, Fletcher said: "It is entirely possible, given our present progressive pollution of the human gene pool through uncontrolled sexual reproduction, that we might have to replicate healthy people to compensate for the spread of genetic diseases."[17]

"It is clear that biological and chemical possibilities for influencing human evolution and development are certain to come," said James F. Crow, of the University of Wisconsin, "probably before we have thought them through. I think the time is here when the subject should be opened and discussed by everyone—not just biologists—with a serious consideration of the consequences of misjudgments as well as the possibilities for good."[18]

The subject certainly has been opened for discussion, and as the pros and cons multiply, society will either adjust, morally and legally, or give way to a new society of supermen.

Dr. Sinsheimer says genetic engineering will give man the power for the first time to cut his ties to the primitive past:

> The alternative, I fear, is a moral and physical stagnation, a repetitive cycle of human hope and human defeat. We are, for better or worse, the one creature with reason. It is the mark of man, and we are committed to its path—to the unending use of reason—to free us from the external tyrannies of nature and the internal constraints of our inheritance. If there be a hidden fatal flaw, if behind reason there is the abyss, then it is our destiny and we can do no better. But it seems to me that all knowledge speaks otherwise.
>
> "The proper study of mankind is man," Pope wrote. He saw with a clear vision, but he was ahead of his time for it is only now that the analytic study of man can properly begin.
>
> We, mankind, are to have the opportunity to design the future of life, to apply intelligence to evolution. This is an astounding chance and infinite challenge.
>
> And, as "darkly wise and rudely great" we climb, arduously out of ignorance, out of shadowed depths, to look back from time to time may help us to understand where we are and to see how far we have come, can help us to sense how very far we may yet advance. In the words written in an old church:
>
> "You are a child of the universe, no less than the trees and the stars. You have a right to be here."[19]

We have a right to be here, as we are now—imperfect but striving to be better—and as we will be tomorrow, men made by other men still guided by the First Force which started it all so long ago.

Notes

CHAPTER 1

1. *World Book Encyclopedia*, 1966, Vol. P, p. 581.
2. This and preceding examples of magic are from Sir James George Frazer, *The Golden Bough* (New York: The Macmillan Company, 1944), pp. 13–33.
3. Will Durant, *The Story of Civilization* (New York: Simon and Schuster, Inc.).
4. *Ibid.*
5. Frazer, pp. 387–389.
6. *Encyclopaedia Britannica*, Vol. XVII, p. 684. Also Dr. Francis Wise, *Youth and Drugs* (New York: Association Press, 1971), p. 14.
7. *Encyclopaedia Britannica*, Vol. XVI, p. 815.
8. Los Angeles *Times*, November 12, 1970.
9. *Ibid.*, January 30, 1972.

CHAPTER 2

1. *Encyclopaedia Britannica*, Vol. IX, p. 371, Vol. IX, p. 395, Vol. V, p. 188B.
2. *Ibid.*, Vol. I, p. 536.
3. *Ibid.*, Vol. XVII, p. 248.
4. *Ibid.*, Vol. XV, p. 199.
5. *Ibid.*, Vol. XVII, p. 891.
6. Henry Still, *The Dirty Animal* (New York: Hawthorn Books, Inc., 1967), p. 17.

7. *Encyclopaedia Britannica*, Vol. XVII, p. 361.

8. *Time* magazine, April 26, 1971, p. 68.

9. Los Angeles *Times*, October 11, 1971, p. 1.

10. Dr. Edward F. Knipling, quoted in Still, p. 241.

11. Minneapolis *Tribune*, October 25, 1971, p. 6.

12. *World Book Encyclopedia*, Vol. H, p. 304.

13. Los Angeles *Times*, October 15, 1971, p. 3.

14. John E. Pike, "Prostaglandins," *Scientific American*, November, 1971, pp. 84–92.

CHAPTER 3

1. Fielding H. Garrison, *History of Medicine* (Philadelphia: W. B. Saunders Company, 1929–1960), pp. 401–402.

2. Sir James George Frazer, *The Golden Bough* (New York: The Macmillan Company, 1944), pp. 546–582.

3. Mark 5:1–17, Confraternity Text.

4. Garrison, pp. 401–402.

5. *Encyclopaedia Britannica*, Vol. XV, p. 263.

6. Garrison, pp. 702–703.

7. *Encyclopaedia Britannica*, Vol. XVIII, p. 667G.

8. *World Book Encyclopedia*, Vol. M, p. 329.

9. *Encyclopaedia Britannica*, Vol. I, pp. 831–832.

10. *The New York Times*, May 20, 1968.

11. *Practitioner* (London), Vol. CXCIX (1967), pp. 825–832.

12. *Journal of the American Medical Association*, Vol. CLXXXI (1962), p. 172.

13. *Ibid.*, Vol. CLXX (1960), pp. 542–557, and Vol. CLXXII (1960), pp. 1502–1513.

14. *Journal of Pharmacy and Pharmacology* (London), Vol. XX, pp. 48–52S.

15. Dr. Andrew I. Malcolm, quoted in Los Angeles *Times*, March 25, 1970, p. 5.

16. *West* magazine, April 25, 1971, pp. 38–39.

17. Dr. Leo E. Hollister and Herbert Kohl, quoted in Los Angeles *Times*, November 24, 1970.

18. *Wall Street Journal*, November 20, 1967.

19. Vasily I. Chernyshov and Dr. Tamara Anatolevna, quoted in Los Angeles *Times*, June 11, 1971, p. 3.

20. Roy G. Spece, Jr., and J. Anthony Kouba, quoted *ibid.*, April 9, 1972.

21. *Wall Street Journal*, November 20, 1967.

22. *Virginia Medical Monthly*, Vol. XCIV (1967), pp. 464–467.

23. *Proceedings of CIBA Foundation Symposium*, London, 1964, pp. 44–61.

24. *Psychopharmacology, a Review of Progress,* 1967, pp. 83–90.

25. *Journal of Nervous and Mental Diseases,* Vol. CXLIV (1967), pp. 421–429.

26. *Lakartidningen* (Sweden), Vol. LXIII (1966), pp. 4973–4980.

27. *Advances in Pharmacology,* Vol. V (1967), pp. 79–108.

28. Desmond King-Hele, quoted in *New Scientist,* February 26, 1970.

29. Dr. Perry London, quoted in Los Angeles *Times,* January 1, 1970.

30. Dr. Frank J. Ayd, Jr., quoted *ibid.,* March 22, 1970.

31. *New Scientist and Science Journal,* September 9, 1971, pp. 560–561.

32. Montreal *Star,* September 20, 1971, p. 35.

33. *World Book Encyclopedia,* Vol. WXYZ, p. 470.

34. *American Journal of Physiology,* quoted in *Time* magazine, October 25, 1971.

CHAPTER 4

1. Christiaan Barnard and Curtis Bell Pepper, *One Life* (New York: The Macmillan Company, 1969), pp. 387, 89, 152.

2. *World Book Encyclopedia,* Vol. T, p. 353.

3. Fielding H. Garrison, *History of Medicine* (Philadelphia: W. B. Saunders Company, 1929–1960), pp. 28–30.

4. *Ibid.,* pp. 54–85.

5. *U.S. News & World Report,* March 13, 1972, p. 25.

6. Garrison, pp. 54–85.

7. *Encyclopaedia Britannica,* Vol. XV, p. 201.

8. Garrison, p. 238.

9. *Britannica Year Book,* 1971, p. 776.

10. Garrison, p. 228.

11. Henry E. Sigerist, *The Great Doctors* (Garden City, N.Y.: Doubleday & Company, Inc., 1958), pp. 201–210, 211–218, 360–363.

12. Garrison, pp. 246–247.

13. *World Book Encyclopedia,* Vol. H, pp. 138–139.

14. *Britannica Year Book,* 1972, p. 451.

15. *Time* magazine, December 7, 1970, p. 72.

16. Los Angeles *Times,* December 7, 1970, p. 5.

17. *Encyclopaedia Britannica,* Vol. XII, pp. 112–113; *World Book Encyclopedia,* Vol. B, pp. 324–325.

18. *Britannica Year Book,* 1963, p. 193.

19. *Britannica Year Book,* 1970, p. 542.

20. *New Scientist and Science Journal,* May 13, 1971, pp. 396–397.

21. Jonathan Swift, quoted in Gustav Eckstein, *The Body Has a Head* (New York: Harper & Row, Publishers, 1970), p. 207.

22. *Britannica Year Book,* 1968, p. 530.

23. Barnard and Pepper, pp. 390–425.

24. *Britannica Year Book,* 1970, p. 496.

25. *New Scientist and Science Journal,* May 13, 1971, pp. 396–397.

26. *Britannica Year Book,* 1971, p. 497.

27. *Ibid.,* p. 477.

28. Los Angeles *Times,* November 8, 1970.

29. *Monsanto* magazine, March, 1969, pp. 1–5.

30. *The New York Times,* June 29, 1970.

31. Dr. Harold Hillman, quoted in *New Scientist,* March 19, 1970, p. 552.

32. *Britannica Year Book,* 1968, p. 528.

33. *U.S. News & World Report,* June 29, 1970, p. 4.

34. Los Angeles *Times,* April 14, 1969.

CHAPTER 5

1. Fielding H. Garrison, *History of Medicine* (Philadelphia: W. B. Saunders Company, 1929–1960), p. 176.

2. *Ibid.,* p. 118.

3. *Ibid.,* p. 177.

4. *Encyclopaedia Britannica,* Vol. XI, p. 791.

5. Garrison, p. 136.

6. London *Times,* April 15, 1857.

7. Garrison, p. 773; *Encyclopaedia Britannica,* Vol. XVI, pp. 445A–445B; *World Book Encyclopedia,* Vol. N–O, p. 328.

8. Garrison, p. 260.

9. *Ibid.,* p. 412.

10. *World Book Encyclopedia,* Vol. WXYZ, p. 449.

11. *Time* magazine, May 10, 1971, p. 65.

12. Los Angeles *Times,* June 25, 1971.

13. *Ibid.,* June 30, 1971.

14. *World Book Encyclopedia,* Vol. H, p. 139.

15. Announcement, National Institutes of Health, June 10, 1969.

16. Minneapolis *Tribune,* January 10, 1972.

17. *Newsweek* magazine, June 1, 1970, p. 54.

18. Eugene E. Horton, speech printed in *APA News,* Fall, 1969.

19. *Time* magazine, April 26, 1971, p. 66.

20. Announcement, Battelle Northwest, July 10, 1970.

21. Los Angeles *Times,* December 26, 1971, p. 3.

22. *Time* magazine, April 26, 1971, p. 66.

23. Stanford *Observer,* February, 1971, p. 4.

24. Dr. Max H. Weil, quoted in Los Angeles *Times,* February 14, 1971.

25. *New Scientist and Science Journal,* February 4, 1971.

26. Los Angeles *Times,* November 27, 1970, Sec. II, p. 15.

27. *Time* magazine, June 7, 1971, p. 70.

28. Los Angeles *Times*, May 16, 1971.

29. Elliot L. Richardson, quoted in *Social Services Outlook*, May, 1971, pp. 1–3.

CHAPTER 6

1. *Wall Street Journal*, April 11, 1969, p. 14.

2. *Britannica Year Book*, 1967, p. 528.

3. Los Angeles *Times*, November 18, 1971, p. 4.

4. *Britannica Year Book*, 1968, p. 514.

5. *Ibid.*, 1969, p. 500.

6. *Ibid.*, 1970, p. 510.

7. *Ibid.*, 1971, p. 494.

8. *Ibid.*, p. 498.

9. *Ibid.*, 1963, p. 544.

10. Los Angeles *Times*, July 16, 1971.

11. *Britannica Year Book*, 1969, p. 506.

12. *Ibid.*, 1967, p. 521.

13. *International Management*, June, 1966, p. 28e.

14. Los Angeles *Times*, May 3, 1971, Pt. I, p. 3.

15. *Report*, Center for Study of Democratic Institutions, December, 1970, p. 13.

16. Los Angeles *Times*, April 7, 1971.

17. *Ibid.*, May 27, 1971.

18. *Report*, Center for Study of Democratic Institutions, December, 1970, p. 13.

19. Los Angeles *Times*, April 15, 1971, Pt. II, p. 1.

20. *Scientific American*, June, 1971, p. 59.

21. *Newsweek* magazine, May 11, 1970.

22. *Ibid.*, April 21, 1969.

23. Dr. Denton Cooley, quoted in *Life* magazine, July, 1969.

24. Announcements, U.S. Department of Health, Education, and Welfare, June 9–19, 1969.

25. Los Angeles *Times*, March 3, 1972.

26. *Ibid.*, August 2, 1971, Pt. I, p. 17.

27. *Ibid.*, May 20, 1971.

28. Dr. Huberto Fernandez-Moran, quoted *ibid.*, June 9, 1971.

29. *Technology Forecasts*, January, 1970, p. 12.

30. Dr. Glenn T. Seaborg, quoted *ibid.*

31. Los Angeles *Times*, December 23, 1969, Pt. II, p. 8.

32. Desmond King-Hele, quoted in *New Scientist*, February 26, 1970, pp. 414–416.

33. Manfred Clynes, quoted in John McHale, *The Future of the Future* (New York: George Braziller, 1969), p. 106.

34. *Newsweek* magazine, April 14, 1969; *New Scientist*, May 8, 1969, p. 277.

CHAPTER 7

1. *World Book Encyclopedia*, Vol. S, p. 626; *Encyclopaedia Britannica*, Vol. I, p. 48.
2. Fielding H. Garrison, *History of Medicine* (Philadelphia: W. B. Saunders Company, 1929–1960), pp. 254–255.
3. *World Book Encyclopedia*, Vol. L, p. 246.
4. *Fortune* magazine, June, 1960, p. 154.
5. *The Physics and Chemistry of Life* (New York: Simon and Schuster, Inc., 1955), pp. 190–210.
6. *Fortune* magazine, May, 1966, p. 155.
7. *World Book Encyclopedia*, Vol. C, p. 250.
8. Gustav Eckstein, *The Body Has a Head* (New York: Harper & Row, Publishers, 1970), p. 154.
9. *World Book Encyclopedia*, Vol. V, p. 332.
10. *Fortune* magazine, May, 1966, pp. 58–65.
11. *Ibid.*, pp. 163–176.
12. *Ibid.*, p. 12.
13. *Ibid.*, p. 13.
14. *New Scientist*, February 27, 1969, pp. 450–452.

CHAPTER 8

1. Curt Stein, "The Continuity of Genetics," *Daedalus*, Fall, 1970, p. 882; *Encylopaedia Britannica*, Vol. XV, pp. 240–241.
2. *Daedalus*, Fall, 1970, pp. 883–884.
3. *Fortune* magazine, June, 1960, p. 157; *Time* magazine, April 19, 1971, p. 34.
4. *Time* magazine, April 19, 1971, p. 34.
5. *Fortune* magazine, June, 1960, pp. 153–158.
6. George W. Beadle, "The New Genetics: The Threads of Life," *Britannica Year Book*, 1964, p. 57.
7. *Time* magazine, April 19, 1971, p. 34.
8. Beadle, pp. 56–57.
9. *Ibid.*, p. 57.
10. Los Angeles *Times*, June 7, 1970, Sec. G, p. 5.
11. *New Scientist and Science Journal*, June 17, 1971, pp. 700–702.
12. *Fortune* magazine, May, 1966, p. 200.
13. Dr. Robert L. Sinsheimer, from a speech quoted in *Engineering and Science* (California Institute of Technology), May, 1968, p. 20.

CHAPTER 9

1. George W. Beadle, "The New Genetics: The Threads of Life," *Britannica Year Book*, 1964, p. 69.
2. *Ibid.*

3. *The Physics and Chemistry of Life* (New York: Simon and Schuster, Inc., 1955), pp. 156–161.

4. *New Scientist and Science Journal*, July 15, 1971, p. 126.

5. *Scientific American*, August, 1965, pp. 88–89.

6. Beadle, pp. 70–71.

7. Los Angeles *Times*, April 2, 1970.

8. *Wall Street Journal*, July 29, 1970.

9. *Ibid.*

10. *Newsweek* magazine, May 18, 1970, pp. 35–36.

11. Beadle, p. 71.

12. Los Angeles *Times*, April 28, 1971, Pt. II, p. 2.

13. Dr. Donald R. Scoby, "Will Population Controls Allow Man to Outsmart the Dinosaurs?" 1970 speech.

14. Dr. Bentley Glass, speech before the Thomas Alva Edison Foundation, Dearborn, Michigan, February 11, 1967.

15. Scoby, speech.

16. Los Angeles *Times*, April 13, 1970, Pt. IV, p. 4, and June 15, 1970, Pt. IV, p. 17.

17. *Life* magazine, August 6, 1971, pp. 19–25.

18. *Report*, University of Chicago, 1970.

19. *Time* magazine, October 25, 1971, p. 59.

CHAPTER 10

1. Dr. Justin J. Stein in Thousand Oaks *News Chronicle*, April 21, 1971, p. 4.

2. *Britannica Year Book*, 1964, p. 537.

3. *Ibid.*, 1965, p. 530.

4. *Ibid.*, 1964, p. 537.

5. Los Angeles *Times*, June 5, 1971, Pt. I, p. 3.

6. Sir Alexander Haddow in *Britannica Year Book*, 1967, p. 508.

7. *Britannica Year Book*, 1964, p. 537.

8. *Ibid.*, 1965, p. 530.

9. *Ibid.*, 1970, pp. 493–496.

10. Los Angeles *Times*, April 18, 1971, Sec. D, p. 1.

11. *Smithsonian Magazine*, 1971; Los Angeles *Times*, April 29, 1971.

12. *Britannica Year Book*, 1964, p. 538.

13. Los Angeles *Times*, April 18, 1971, Sec. D, p. 1.

14. Thousand Oaks *News Chronicle*, April 21, 1971, p. 4.

15. Fielding H. Garrison, *History of Medicine* (Philadelphia: W. B. Saunders Company, 1929–1960), p. 391.

16. Los Angeles *Times*, April 18, 1971, Sec. D, p. 1.

17. *Ibid.*, April 4, 1971.

18. University of California announcement, April 15, 1969.

19. Los Angeles *Times*, July 3, 1971, p. 1.

20. *Ibid.*, December 6, 1971, p. 1.

21. *Proceedings*, National Academy of Sciences, Vol. 64, p. 1087.

22. *New Scientist and Science Journal*, April 29, 1971.

23. *Newsweek* magazine, June 29, 1970.

24. *New Scientist*, January 22, 1970.

25. *New Scientist and Science Journal*, February 18, 1971, p. 396.

26. *Newsweek* magazine, May 12, 1969, p. 76.

27. Los Angeles *Times*, April 6, 1969, Sec. F, p. 1.

28. *Newsweek* magazine, May 12, 1969, p. 76.

29. Los Angeles *Times*, July 14, 1971, and March 28, 1972.

30. *New Scientist and Science Journal*, May 3, 1971, p. 397.

31. Los Angeles *Times*, March 29, 1972.

32. *Ibid.*, April 6, 1971.

33. *Ibid.*, February 14, 1971, Sec. F, p. 1.

CHAPTER 11

1. *Britannica Year Book*, 1964, p. 552.

2. *Johns Hopkins Magazine*, Spring, 1968, p. 1; *Resident Physician*, January, 1968, p. 86.

3. *Geriatric Focus*, Vol. VIII, No. 17 (October 15, 1969), p. 1.

4. Los Angeles *Times*, May 16, 1971, Sec. G, p. 1.

5. *Ibid.*, November 30, 1970, p. 5.

6. Thousand Oaks *News Chronicle*, March 24, 1971, p. 3.

7. *The Gerontologist*, Vol. VIII, No. 3 (Autumn, 1968), p. 148.

8. United Press International dispatch, May 18, 1971.

9. *Wisconsin Medical Journal*, Vol. LXVII, No. 2 (1968), pp. 117–120.

10. *Psychosomatics*, August 4, 1967, p. 69.

11. Bernard Strehler, "Ten Myths about Aging," *The Center Magazine* (Center for Study of Democratic Institutions, Santa Barbara, California), Vol. II, No. 4 (July 19, 1970), pp. 41–48.

12. *Johns Hopkins Magazine*, Spring, 1968, pp. 13–20.

13. *New Scientist*, February 26, 1970, pp. 414–416.

14. *Ibid.*, December 11, 1969, pp. 549–551.

15. Associated Press dispatch, February 23, 1968.

16. *The New York Times*, April 30, 1969; *Newsweek* magazine, May 12, 1969, p. 77.

17. Los Angeles *Times*, April 15, 1971, p. 7.

18. *Newsweek* magazine, March 24, 1969.

CHAPTER 12

1. Dr. James D. Watson, quoted in Los Angeles *Times*, January 29, 1971, Pt. I, p. 6.

2. Dr. Robert L. Sinsheimer, in *The Far Reach of Science* (California Institute of Technology, 1968).

3. Dr. Marshall W. Nirenberg in statement by the National Institutes of Health, 1970.

4. *Newsweek* magazine, June 1, 1970, p. 46.

5. *New Scientist*, March 27, 1969, p. 698.

6. Los Angeles *Times*, January 1, 1970, Pt. I, p. 25.

7. *Reports*, University of Chicago, Vol. XX, No. 2 (Fall, 1970), pp. 1–10.

8. *Nature New Biology*, Vol. 230, p. 5.

9. *Proceedings*, National Academy of Sciences, Vol. LXV, p. 911.

10. *Time* magazine, November 23, 1970, p. 52; *New Scientist and Science Journal*, January 21, 1971, pp. 124–125.

11. *Reports*, University of Chicago, Vol. XX, No. 2 (Fall, 1970), pp. 1–10.

12. Dr. James Bonner, in *The Far Reach of Science*.

13. Roscoe Drummond in Farmington (New Mexico) *Daily Times*, February 22, 1971, p. 2.

14. *Time* magazine, April 19, 1971, p. 42.

15. Los Angeles *Times*, June 20, 1969, Pt. I, p. 15.

16. *The Frozen Cell*, proceedings of the CIBA Foundation symposium, 1970 (Churchill Press, 1970).

17. Los Angeles *Times*, June 16, 1971, Sec. 3, p. 1.

18. *Look* magazine, May 18, 1971, pp. 83–88.

19. *Time* magazine, April 19, 1971, p. 42.

20. Los Angeles *Times*, January 29, 1971, Pt. I, p. 6.

21. *Ibid.*, June 16, 1971, Sec. 3, p. 1.

22. *Ibid.*, April 18, 1972, Pt. IV, p. 3.

23. *New Scientist*, November 13, 1969, pp. 350–351.

24. Los Angeles *Times*, May 17, 1971, Pt. IV, p. 1.

25. *Technology Forecasts*, January, 1970, p. 12.

26. *Britannica Year Book*, 1971, p. 484.

27. Los Angeles *Times*, July 25, 1971, p. 1.

28. *Technology Forecasts*, January, 1970, p. 12.

29. Los Angeles *Times*, May 17, 1971, Pt. IV, p. 1.

CHAPTER 13

1. Joshua Lederberg, testimony before House Appropriations Subcommittee, June 10, 1970.

2. Dr. Margaret Mead, quoted in *The Tidings*, June 25, 1971, p. 3.

3. *New Scientist*, February 20, 1969, p. 381.

4. Henry Still, *Man: The Next 30 Years* (New York: Hawthorn Books, Inc., 1969), p. 142.

5. Victor K. McElheny, quoted in *Technology Review* (Massachusetts Institute of Technology), July–August, 1970, p. 2.

6. Statement by the National Institutes of Health, 1971.

7. *Center Report* (Center for Study of Democratic Institutions, Santa Barbara, California), December, 1970, p. 12; *Time* magazine, April 19, 1971.

8. *Reports*, University of Chicago, Vol. XX, No. 2 (Fall, 1970), pp. 1–10.

9. Los Angeles *Times*, November 23, 1969, pp. 1, 25.

10. *New Scientist and Science Journal*, January 21, 1971, pp. 124–125.

11. Dr. Bentley Glass, speech before the Thomas Alva Edison Foundation, Dearborn, Michigan, February 11, 1967.

12. Lederberg, testimony before House Appropriations Subcommittee, June 10, 1970. Also Lederberg, "Orthobiosis, the Perfection of Man," paper presented at Nobel Symposium, Stockholm, September, 1969.

13. Los Angeles *Times*, October 17, 1971, Sec. F, p. 1.

14. Stanford *Observer*, April, 1972, p. 3.

15. Los Angeles *Times*, November 23, 1970, Pt. I, p. 3.

16. *Time* magazine, April 19, 1971, p. 52.

17. Joseph Fletcher, quoted in Los Angeles *Times*, May 20, 1971, Pt. IV, p. 11.

18. James F. Crow, quoted in *BioScience*, December, 1966, p. 867.

19. Dr. Robert L. Sinsheimer, *The Far Reach of Science* (California Institute of Technology, 1968).

Bibliography

Barnard, Christiaan, and Pepper, Curtis Bell. *One Life*. New York: The Macmillan Company, 1969.

Butterfield, Herbert. *The Origins of Modern Science*. New York: The Macmillan Company, 1957.

Daedalus. Fall, 1970.

Eckstein, Gustav. *The Body Has a Head*. New York: Harper & Row, Publishers, 1970.

Ettinger, Robert C. W. *The Prospect of Immortality*. Garden City, N.Y.: Doubleday & Company, Inc., 1964.

Frazer, Sir George. *The Golden Bough*. 1-volume abridged edition. New York: The Macmillan Company, 1944.

Garrison, Fielding H. *History of Medicine*. Philadelphia: W. B. Saunders Company, 1929–1960.

McHale, John. *The Future of the Future*. New York: George Braziller, 1969.

The Physics and Chemistry of Life. New York: Simon and Schuster, Inc., 1955.

Sigerist, Henry E. *The Great Doctors*. Garden City, N.Y.: Doubleday & Company, Inc., 1958.

Thomson, Sir George. *The Foreseeable Future*. New York: Cambridge University Press, 1955.

Wise, Francis. *Youth and Drugs*. New York: Association Press, 1971.

The World in 1984. Baltimore, Md.: Penguin Books, Inc., 1965.

Index

Abbott, Maude, 58
Abcor, Inc., 79
Abiogenesis, theory of, 111
Abortion, 139, 140, 149, 151
  legal sanction of, 155
ACTH, 28
Acupuncture, 54–55
Adenine, 127, 128, 129
Adrenaline, 27–28
Aesculapius, legend of, 55
Aging, process of, 178–198
  myths and, 186–190
Air pollution, 166
Albert, Prince, 140
Albinoism, 138
Alchemy, 15–17
Alcohol, 4, 9, 35, 146–147
  as an anesthetic, 53
  consumption (U.S.), 11
  religion and, 9–10
  treatment for alcoholism, 36
Aldosterone, 28
Alvarez, Dr. Walter, 152
Amaurotic idiocy, 144–145
American Aging Association, 184
American Cancer Society, 164–165, 172
American Indians, 10–11, 25
American Medical Association, 165
American Psychiatric Association, 42
American Social Health Association, 12
American Thoracic Society, 102
Amethyst, 6
Aminazine, 40–41
Amino acids, 121
  number of, 116
Amniocentesis, 153, 214
Amoebic dysentery, 20
Amphetamines, 37, 147
  number of, 39
  use of, 36, 42–43
Amulets, 6, 53
Anatolevna, Dr. Tamara, 41
Anectine, 41
Anesthesia, science of, 58, 76
Animalculae, 21
Anne, Queen, 56–57
Antihistamines, 25
Antilymphocytic serum (ALS), 64
Antireticulocytotoxic serum, 188
Aphrodisiacs, 8
Arabs, 73
Argonne National Laboratory, 80
Aristotle, 15–16, 18, 55, 111, 112

Arms, artificial, 92–93, 94
  battery-powered, 93
Arnold of Villanova, 16
Arnott, James, 197
Artery replacements, 99
Artificial insemination, 210–211, 215
Asparaginase, 163
Aspirin, discovery of, 24
Astrology, 7
Atabrine, 20
Atherosclerosis, 61
Atomic bombs, 77, 160
Atomic Energy Commission, 80, 104
Autosomal chromosomes, 136–137
Aversion therapy, 38
Avery, Oswald T., 126
Ayd, Dr. Frank J., Jr., 45
Azothioprine, 64

Babylon, 53–54, 73
Bacon, Roger, 16
Bahnson, Dr. Claus, 175
Baker, Dr. Carl G., 167, 176
Balaclava, Battle of, 74
Baluda, Dr. Marcel, 167–168
Barbital, 36
Barbiturates, 37, 147
  use of, 36
Barnard, Dr. Christiaan, 51–52, 59, 64
Barrows, Dr. Charles H., 192–193
Battelle Memorial Institute, 82–83
BCG, 174
Beadle, George W., 126, 130
Beatles, 47, 212
Beckwith, Jonathan, 204, 224
Bedford, Dr. James H., 197
Bedlam (asylum), 31–32, 33
Beers, Clifford W., 34
Behavior Control (London), 44–45
Beijerinck, Martinus Willem, 114
Benson, Dr. Herbert, 47
Benzer, Seymour, 126
Berger, Hans, 77
Beriberi, 26
Beutler, Dr. Ernest, 215
Bible, 8, 110, 180
Bilitch, Dr. Michael, 99–100
Biofeedback
  meaning of, 46
  meditation and, 47–48
  yoga, 47
Bionics, science of, 81
Bioreceivers, 96–97

Birnstiel, Dr. Max, 204
Black Death, 19
Blaug, Seymour, 12
Blood, artificial, 91
Blood, synthetic, 98–99
Bloodletting, 53
Blood-typing, 65–66
Blood-vessel grafts, 99
Blue babies, first operation for, 58–59
Bone marrow transplants, 60
Bones, artificial, 91
Bonner, Dr. James, 132–133, 189, 194, 208–209, 217–218
Boothe, Dr. James J., 24
Borgaonkar, Dr. Digamber, 143
Brain control experiments, 98
Brain tumors, determination of, 77
Brain waves, manipulation of, 45–46
Brave New World (Huxley), 37, 218, 223
British Medical Association, 195
Bronze Age, 53
Bruce, Sarah Ann, 171
BUdR (5bromodeosyuridine), 171
Bufotenine, 36
Burkitt's lymphoma, 162, 163, 168

Caffeine, 42
Calgary General Hospital, 93
California Institute of Technology, 126, 132–133, 135, 142, 189, 194, 202, 208, 227
California Medical Facility at Vacaville, 41
California Supreme Court, 41
Calvin, Melvin, 167
Cambridge University, 80, 127, 213
Camphor, 33
Cancer, 32, 76, 77, 96, 157–177, 208
  body's immune mechanism and, 172–174
  cause of, 165–177
  cigarettes and, 166, 182
  deaths per year (U.S.), 158
  drugs tested against, 161–162
  early detection of, 164–165
  forms of, 159
  hormone therapy, 162
  meaning of, 158
  metastasis process, 160
  radiation therapy, 160–161
  rate of cure, 165
  rate of growth, 159
  surgery, 159–160
  virus and, 167–170
Cancer Prevention Center (Chicago), 87
Cannibalism, 5
Carbolic acid, 58
Carbon, 11, 78
  as prosthetic material, 93
Carnegie Institution, 126
Cartier, Jacques, 25
Castration, 54, 144

Cavalieri, Ercole, 167
Cavendish Laboratory, 127
Cell-therapy technique, 13
Cells, body, 112–115
  amino acids, 116, 121
  core and code, 122–135
  enzymes, 116–118, 119
  fertilization, 118–119
  genetic defects, 136–156
  intellectual energies of, 113
  meiosis, 114, 141
  protein molecules, 115–116
  replacement of, 116–117
  size of, 113
Center for the Critically Ill (University of Southern California), 85
Chain, Ernst Boris, 15
Chemstrand Corporation, 99
Chernyshov, Vasily I., 41
Cherry, Dr. Sheldon H., 153
Chicken pox, treatment of, 24
Children's Hospital Medical Center, 175
Child's sex, predicting, 215–216
Chimney Sweepers Act of 1788, 165
China, 54–55
Chloroform, 58
Chlorpromazine, 35
Cholera, 24
Choriocarcinoma, 162
Chromosomal RNA, 132–133
Cine coronary angiography, 77
City of Hope Medical Center, 215
Cleveland Clinic, 79
Clinical thermometer, invention of, 76
Cloriocarcinoma, 163
Clynch, George, 93
Clynes, Manfred, 105
Cobalt 60, 160–161
Coca-Cola, 12
Cocaine, 12
Codeine, 11
Cod-liver oil, 25
Coffee, drinking, 146
Cole, Dandridge, 106
Collagen, 96, 115
Color blindness, 141
Colorado Medical School, 172
Columbia University, 125, 213
Columbus, Christopher, 3, 6
Comfort, Dr. Alex, 181, 193–194
Committee on Life Sciences and Social Policy, 223
Congenital insanity, 34
Constantine, Emperor, 6
Contact lenses, 95
Cooley, Dr. Denton, 100–101
Cooper, Dr. Irving S., 197–198
Cooper, Dr. Theodore, 102
Corneal transplants, 95
Cornell University, 134, 171, 217
Correns, Carl, 124
Cortisone, 28, 64

Craig, S. R., 162
Crete (ancient), 6
Crewé, Albert V., 204
Crick, Francis H. C., 127–131, 228
Crimean War, 74
Crow, James F., 228–229
Cryonics, 197
Cryonics Society, 197
Cryosurgery, 198
Curie, Marie and Pierre, 160
Cybernetic Anthropomorphous Machine System (CAMS), 105
Cyclic adenyl acid (cyclic AMP), 28
Cytosine, 127, 128, 129

Danielli, Dr. James F., 207, 218, 224
Dark Ages, 13, 16, 18–19
Darvall, Denise Ann, 51–52
Darwin, Charles, 112, 123, 125
De Fabrica Humani Corporia (Vesalius), 57
Death penalty, abolition of, 41
Death rate, 181–182
DeBakey, Dr. Michael E., 68, 101
Diechman, John, 83
Delbruck, Max, 126
Demonic possession, 32–33
Deoxyribonucleic acid (DNA), 63, 119, 123–135, 167, 193, 201, 204, 206, 208, 228
    discovery of, 123–124, 125, 126
    Watson-Crick theory, 127–131
Depression, 37, 38
    treatment of, 36
Desamyl, 42–43
De Vries, Hugo, 124
Diabetes, 27, 144, 147, 151, 182
Diacumakos, Elaine, 205
Diarrhea, 56
Dichlorodiphenyl-trichloroethane (DDT), 25
Diethrich, Dr. Edward B., 69
Diethylstilbestrol, 161
Dionysus, worship of, 9–10
Dioscorides, 18
Diphtheria, 21
    treatment of, 22–23
Dix, Dorothea Lynde, 34
Dmochowsky, Dr. Leon, 168
DOM, 43
Dorfman, Dr. Albert, 153–154
Drug abuse, 37–39
Dulbecco, Renato, 170–171
Durant, Will, 6
Dysentery, 23, 24, 25

Eastern Pennsylvania Psychiatric Institute, 175
Eckert, Dr. Prosper, 86–87
Eckhart, Walter, 170–171
Edelman, Gerald M., 63
Edinburgh University, 204

Edwards, Dr. Robert C., 213
Egypt (ancient), 16, 17, 53, 55
Einstein, Albert, 221
Einthoven, Willem, 77
Eisenhower, Dwight D., 196
Electric shock treatments, 35
Electrocardiograms (EKG), 77, 82
Electrocardiographs, 77
Electroencephalogram (EEG), 77
Electrolour, 99
Electronic devices, computer controlled, 85
Elixir of life, search for, 3–13
El Welid, Caliph, 73
Embryo implant, birth by, 214–215
Embryonal testicular cancer, 163
Emory University, 173
Encyclopaedia Britannica, 86
Environmental Services Laboratory, 104
Epilepsy, 36, 196
    control of, 97
    diagnosis of, 77
Epinephrine, 27–28
Erasistratus, 55–56
Eron, Lawrence, 224
Ether, 58
Euler, Ulf S. von, 29
Euthanasia, 195, 196
Evolution, theory of, 112–113
Evolution of the Superman (Clynes), 105
Ewing's sarcoma, 163
Examination cramming, 37
Exorcism, ceremony of, 32–33
Eye cornea transplants, 60

Fabiola, 73
Fambrough, Doublas, 132
Fernandez-Moran, Dr. Huberto, 103
Fertility drugs, 216
Fingers, artificial, 105
Fleming, Alexander, 14
Fletcher, Joseph, 228
Florey, Howard W., 14
Florida, discovery of, 3–4
Folkman, Dr. Judah, 175
Fox, Sidney, 121
Fracastoro, Girolomo, 21
Frazer, Sir James, 9, 32
Freud, Sigmund, 34
Friese, Gernot, 91

Galactosemia, 154
Galen of Pergamum, 18, 57, 58
Gamma globulin, isolation of, 63
Gardner, Dr. Murray B., 168
Gascoyne's powder, 20
Geier, Mark, 154–155
Gene, first synthetic, 204
General Electric Company, 105
Genetic abnormality, 136–156
    karyotyping, 155–156
    number of persons born with, 139

pairs of chromosomes, 137
sickle cell, 137–138
XYY syndrome, 142–144, 152
Georgetown University, 168–169
Gerhardt, Charles, 24
Geyer, Dr. Robert P., 98
Gibbon, Dr. John H., 78
Gilbert, D. A., 171
Glasky, Dr. Alvin J., 42
Glass, Dr. Bentley, 148–149, 224–225
Glaucoma, 84
Glenn, John, 212
Goitrous cretinism, 144
Goldblatt, Maurice W., 29
Golden Bough, The (Frazer), 9
Goldwater, Barry, 220
Gonadotrophin, 216
Gonorrhea, 23
Good, Dr. Robert A., 172–173
Goodlin, Dr. Robert, 218
Gordon, Dr. Paul, 23–24
Gowans, James, 174
Greece (ancient), 6, 16, 17–18, 55–56, 73
Guanine, 127, 128, 129
Gurdon, John, 208, 217

Haberlandt, Gottlieb, 217
Hair grafts, 60–61
Hallucinogenic drugs, 36–37, 147
Haloperidol, 41
Hands, artificial, bioelectrically operated, 93
Hardman, Dr. Harold F., 196
Harman, Dr. Denham, 184–185
Harmison, Dr. Lowell T., 102
Harris, Henry, 205
Harvard University, 47, 98, 120–121, 175, 204, 213, 224
Harvey, William, 58
Havez, Dr. E. S. E., 212, 214
Health-care system, 88–89
Health insurance, cost of, 88
Hearing aids, 94
Heart, artificial, 100–102
Heart-lung machine, 78–79, 88, 98, 102–103
Heart transplants, 51–52, 64
donors, 60
number of, 59
Hebrews (ancient), 54
Hemicorporectomy, 94
Hemophilia, 65, 140–141, 152
Henry VIII, King, 31
Heon, Kwang W., 207
Heraclitus, 88
Herbert, Sidney, 74
Heroin, 38, 147
Herophilus, 55–56
Herrick, James B., 58
Hershey, Alfred D., 126
Hertwig, Oskar, 124
Hillman, Dr. Harold, 67–68

Hindus, 5, 47, 54
Hines Veterans Hospital, 183
Hipbones, artificial, 96
Hippie culture, 12, 39
Hippocrates, 17–18, 55, 215
Hippocratic Oath, 18
Hodgkin's disease, 161, 163
Hofmann, Albert, 36
Holland, Scott, 205
Hollister, Dr. Leo E., 40
Hollywood Presbyterian Hospital, 85
Homer, 55
Hormones, 27–29, 30
cancer therapy, 162
Horn, Dr. Dan, 166
Horton, Eugene E., 81
Hospitals
historical background, 70–75
maintenance per person, 87
modern surgery in, 70–72
new body-shop techniques, 75–87
number of (U.S.), 87
religious orders, 73, 74
Hôtel Dieu, 73
Huang, Ruchih, 132
Huebner, Dr. Robert J., 168, 169
Humphrey, Dr. Loren J., 173
Hunter, John, 57–58
Huntington's chorea, 145
Huxley, Aldous, 37, 218, 223
Hyaluronic acid, 118
Hyaluronidase, 118
Hydrocortisone, 28
Hypnotism, 34

IAP, 205
Iatrochemistry, 17
Iliad (Homer), 55
Illinois Industrial School for Boys, 41
Imhotep, 17
Immortality, quest for, 4–5
Immunoglobulins, 62
Immunotherapy, 64–65
Imuran, 172
Industrial Revolution, 12
Infant mortality, 56–57, 87–88
decrease in, 57
Influenza, treatment of, 24
Inquisition, 8, 123
Insane people, public exhibition of, 32
Insomnia, 36
Institute for Cancer Research (Philadelphia), 63
Institute for the Future (Connecticut), 104
Institute for Muscle Research, 164
Institute of Society, Ethics and the Life Sciences, 227
Institution for the Care of Sick Gentlewomen in Distressed Circumstances, 74
Insulin, 27, 147

Insulin-shock treatment, 35
International Chemical and Nuclear Corporation, 42
Iodine, radioactive, 77–78
Ipecac, 20
Iron Age, 53
Isabella, Queen, 73
Isoprinosine, 23–24
Isotopes, 77–78

Jansen, Zacharias, 21
Jenner, Edward, 21, 22
John XXII, Pope, 7
Johns Hopkins University, 68–69, 143, 192
Joints, artificial, 96
Jung, C. G., 16, 34

Karp, Haskell, 100–101
Karyotype chromosome map, 155–156
Kass, Leon, 223
Khorana, D. H. Gobind, 131, 204, 222
Kidney transplants, 60, 66, 172
Kidneys, artificial, 79–80
King, Dr. Paul H., 83
King-Hele, Desmond, 44, 104, 193
Klein, Dr. Marvin, 84
Klinefelder's syndrome, 142
Klinkmann, Dr. Horst, 102
Knee, electric, 93
Knipling, Dr. Edward F., 25
Kohl, Herbert, 40
Koran, 215
Kornberg, Arthur, 126, 128–129
Kornevac, Dr. Elena A., 175
Kouba, J. Anthony, 41–42
Kraepelin, Emil, 34
Krasnov, Dr. Mikhail, 95
Kurzrok, Dr. Raphael, 29

Laennec, Dr. René Théophile Hyacinthe, 76
Lambert, Edward, 136
Lande, Dr. A. J., 102–103
Landsteiner, Karl, 65
La Tene culture, 53
Laughing gas (nitrous oxide), 58
Laurens, Dr. Paul, 100
Lawn, Dr. Lawrence, 80
L-dopa, 42
Leaf cells, size of, 113
Lederberg, Dr. Joshua, 126, 176–177, 219, 220, 225–227
Legs, artificial, 92
Leopold, Prince, 140
Lepers, 32
Leukemia, 160, 162–163
Liddicote, Dr. John, 69
Lieb, Dr. Charles C., 29
Life, meaning of, 109–121
Life expectancy rate, 181

Light Brigade, charge of, 74
Limbs, artificial, 92, 94
Lincoln, Dr. Thomas L., 88, 181
Liotta, Dr. Domingo, 101
Lipofuscin, 192
Lister, Dr. Joseph, 58
Livers, artificial, 103
London, Dr. Perry, 44–45
London, Plague of, 1664-1665, 19
Lorch, Joan, 207
Ludwigsburg District Hospital (Germany), 91
Lung cancer, 197
    cigarettes and, 166, 182
    death rate, 158, 166
    radiotherapy treatment, 161
Lung transplants, 60
Lymphogranuloma, 24
Lysenko, T. D., 125
Lysergic acid diethylamide (LSD), 12, 44, 147, 225
    discovery of, 36
    trips, 37
Lysozyme, 62

McAllister, Dr. Robert M., 168
Macbeth (Shakespeare), 7
McCollum, Elmer, 25
MacDonald, Dr. Norman, 78
McElheny, Victor K., 222
McKhann, Dr. Charles F., 173
McLean, Robert E., 144
Magic
    during Dark Ages, 6–8
    during Middle Ages, 7–8
    primitive, 6
Magnesium pemoline, 43
Magnus, Albertus, 16
Mahkov, Alexander, 4
Málaga, siege of, 73
Malaria, 20, 25
Malcolm, Dr. Andrew I., 39
Marcellus of Bordeaux, 5
Marijuana, 11–12, 147, 196
    first use of, 10
    outlawed, 12
Martell, Dr. Michael J., 24
Mary Hitchcock Memorial Hospital, 84–85
Massachusetts General Hospital, 81
Massachusetts Institute of Technology, 131, 222
Matalon, Dr. Reuben, 153
Materia Medica (Dioscorides), 18
Mayview Mental Hospital, 146
Mead, Margaret, 219
Mechanical pain controllers, 96–97
Medical College of Milwaukee, 196
Medical Counterpoint, 45
Medical Research Council Group on Aging, 181

Medicine
    development of, 17–22
    prescientific, 17–18
Meditation, 46–48
    biofeedback and, 47–48
    transcendental, 47
Melancholia, treatment of, 33–34
Melling, Ernest, 195–196
Memory devices, 86–87
Mendel, Gregor Johann, 112, 122–123, 124, 151
Menelaus, King of Sparta, 55
Menninger Foundation, 46
Meprobamate, 43
Merril, Carl, 154–155
Mescaline, 36, 147
Mesmer, Franz Anton, 34
Mesopotamia (ancient), 17, 53
Methamphetamine, 37–38
Methodist Hospital (Houston), 69
Methotrexate, 162
Microscope, first, 21
Middle Ages
    alchemy, 15–17
    magic, 7–8
    medicine, 18
Miescher, Friedrich, 123–124, 125
Miller, Dr. Neal E., 46
Miller, S. L., 121
Mrs. Winslow's Soothing Syrup, 11
Mongolism, 141–142
Montanini, Dr. Gennaro, 216–217
Mood control, synthetic, 97
Morgagni, Giovanni Battista, 57–58
Morgan, Thomas Hunt, 125
Morphine, 11
Morton, Dr. Donald, 174
Moscona, Dr. Aron A., 208, 224
Mosher, Ralph S., 105
Mt. Sinai School of Medicine, 104
Mucopolysaccharides, 153
Muller, Hermann J., 126
Muscular dystrophy, 141
Mystics, religious, 47

Narcolepsy, 36
National Academy of Science, 223
National Aeronautics and Space Administration (NASA), 81, 206
National Cancer Institute, 167, 168, 169, 174, 176
National Clearinghouse for Smoking and Health, 166
National Council on Alcoholism, 146–147
National Foundation of Old Age Pensioners, 195–196
National Heart and Lung Institute, 79, 102
Native American Church, 10
Natural Science Society, 123
Neel, Dr. James V., 152

Neolithic Age, 53
New York Academy of Sciences, 103
New York Times, The, 67
New York University, 131, 224
Nickel, V. L., 94
Nicotinic acid (niacin), 27
Niehans, Dr. Paul, 13
Nightingale, Florence, 74–75
Nine, Mrs. Hatice, 180
Nirenberg, Marshall, 130, 202–203, 222–223
Nitrous oxide, 58
Nixon, Richard M., 54–55, 176, 177, 184, 212
Norris, Arthur, 191
North Dakota State University, 148
Nufer, Jacob, 57

Oak Ridge Associated Universities (Tennessee), 78
Obesity, 184
Opium, 11, 33
Organ transplants, 51–69
    banks for, 69
    immunotherapy, 64–65
    problem of, 61–69
Organic foods, 27
Oxford University, 14–15, 174, 205, 208, 217

Pacemakers, 99–100
    nuclear powered, 100
    radiation interference, 100
Paloucek, Dr. Frank, 87
Pap test, 164–165
Papanicolaou, George, 164
Paracelsus, 17
Pare, Ambroise, 57
Paris Asylum for Men, 34
Parkinson's disease, 36, 42
Pascua florida, 3
Pasteur, Louis, 21–22, 58, 112
Pauling, Linus, 126–127
Pecora, Pauline, 205
Peg legs, 90
Pellagra, prevention of, 27
Pemberton, John S., 12
Penicillin, discovery of, 14–15
Penicillium notatum, 14
Pentobarbital, 36
Petricciani, John, 154–155
Petrucci, Dr. Daniele, 213
Peyote, religious use of, 10–11
Pharmacies, beginning of, 17
Pharmacopoeia, 20
Phenalzine sulfate, 38
Phenobarbital, 36
Phenylketonuria, 144
Philosophers' stone, 16, 30, 180
Pierce's Golden Medical Discovery, 11
Pinel, Philippe, 34
Pinneo, L. R., 98

Pivnica, Dr. Armand H., 100
Plagues, 19–20, 21
Plastic blood vessels, 99
Plastic corneas, implanted, 95
Plastic surgery, 60–61
Polio vaccine, discovery of, 22
Poliomyelitis, 22, 90, 181
Polyurethane plastic valves, 99
Ponce de León, Juan, 3–4, 180
Pontifical Academy of Science, 13
Pope, Alexander, 135
Pott, Percival, 165
Pravda, 4
Prednisone, 64
Preludin, 43–44
Pribram, Karl H., 227
Priori, Elizabeth S., 168
Prohibition, 11
Prontosil, 23
Prostaglandins, discovery of, 29–30
Prosthetics, 90–106
Protein molecules, 115–116, 121
    smallest known, 116
Psoriasis, 162
Psychosomatics, 186
Pudenz, Dr. Robert H., 96–97
Purdue University, 126

Quakers, 34
Queen Charlotte's Hospital (London), 216
Quinine, 20, 24

Radar, 100
Radiation, 100, 114, 138, 160–161
Radioisotopes, 77
Radium, discovery of, 160
Rand Corporation, 88, 181
Rasmussen, John, 83
Ravin, Dr. Arnold W., 204–205
Razavi, Dr. Lawrence, 143
Redi, Francesco, 111
Rehabilitation Institute of Montreal, 93
Reil, Dr. Johann Christian, 33
Renaissance, 111
Reserpine, 35
Rhapsodies (Reil), 33
Rhinoceros horn, 7
Ribonucleic acid (RNA), 119, 129–130,
    132, 133–134, 167, 186, 194, 204
Richardson, Elliot L., 88–89
Rickets, 26, 141
Ritalin (methylphenidate-hydrochloride),
    39–40
Rock, Dr. John, 213
Rockefeller Institute, 126
Rockefeller University, 46, 63
Rocky Mountain spotted fever, 24
Roentgen, Wilhelm C., 76, 160
Roman Catholic Church, 74, 228
Roman Empire, 5, 18, 25, 56, 73, 215

Rose, Mrs. Marilyn, 24
Rosenberg, E. W., 162
Royal Aircraft Establishment, 44, 193
Royal Jennerian Society, 21
Royal Society of Health (England), 195
Russell, Bertrand, 195

Sabin, Albert, 22
Sakel, Manfred, 35
Salem witchcraft hysteria, 8
Salk, Dr. Jonas E., 22, 212
Salk Institute, 170
Sanctorious, 76
Saturnalia, 9–10
Schizophrenia, 36
    treatment of, 35, 43–44
Schlesinger, Dr. Lee H., 183
Scoby, Dr. Donald R., 148, 150–151
Scurvy, 25
Seaborg, Dr. Glenn T., 104
Select Society for Seeking Scientists,
    Saints, and Sinners (Baltimore),
    190–192
Selikoff, Dr. Irvin J., 104
Sessa, Dr. Grazia, 131
Sex hormones, 28
Shakespeare, William, 7
Shelden, Dr. C. Hunter, 96
Shettles, Dr. Landrum B., 213
Shingles, treatment of, 24
Shock, Dr. Nathan W., 184, 190–193
Shumway, Dr. Norman E., 59, 60, 66–67,
    69
Siberian mountain oil, 4
Sickle cell genes, 137–138
Silagi, Dr. Selma, 151
Sillo-Seidel, Dr. George, 211
Silov, Melvin R., 83
Simon, Dr. Lee, 63
Sinsheimer, Dr. Robert L., 135, 202, 227,
    229
Skin cells, size of, 113
Sloan-Kettering Institute, 205
Smallpox, 21
    vaccine, discovery of, 62
Snake oil, 4
Solomon, Dr. George F., 175
Soma, 37
Sones, Dr. F. Mason, Jr., 77
Soranus of Ephesus, 56
Sorcery, 6, 8
South American Indians, 20
Southern California Law Review, 41
Spallanzini, Lazzaro, 111–112
Spece, Roy G., Jr., 41–42
Speed (methamphetamine), 37–38
Sperm banks, 211–212
Spontaneous generation, doctrine of, 111,
    120
Sporting events, drugs and, 38
Sprenger, Jacob, 8

Stanford University, 40, 59, 60, 66–67, 69, 85, 98, 101–102, 126, 143, 175, 176–177, 218, 225
Stanley, Wendell, 115
Staph Rose, 24
Starzl, Dr. Thomas E., 68, 172
State University of New York, 148–149, 207
Stein, Dr. Justin J., 165
Stellenbosch University, 68–69
Steptoe, Patrick C., 213
Sterilization, 149
Stern, Francis H., 185–186
Stern, Dr. Herbert, 227–228
Stethoscope, invention of, 76
Steward, Frederick C., 134, 217
Stillbirths, 139
Stimulants, 44
Stone Age, 53
Stones, veneration of, 4, 5–6
STP, 43
Strehler, Bernard, 186–190
Strontium, radioactive, 78
Sturtevant, Alfred H., 126
Succinylcholine chloride, 41
Suicide rate, 182
    drug-related, 38
Sulfonamide drugs, introduction of, 23
Sumeria, 55
Surgery, 51–69
    cancer, 159–160
    earliest known, 52–53
    historical background, 52–58
    modern techniques, 70–72
    organ transplants, 51–52, 58–69
Sutherland, Dr. Earl W., Jr., 28
Svedberg, The, 116
Swan, Dr. Henry, 59
Swift, Jonathan, 63
Swiss agammaglobulinemia, 60
Syphilis, 23, 34
Szent-Gyorgyi, Dr. Albert, 164

Talmud, 215
Taoism, 16
Tatum, Edward L., 126
Tay-Sachs disease, 152–153
Technology Review, 222
Teilhard de Chardin, Pierre, 228
Tele-Diagnosis system, 80–81
Temin, Dr. Howard, 170
Terasaki, Dr. Paul I., 66
Test-tube baby, 201–202, 213–218
Thalidomide babies, 147–148
Theodosius I, Emperor, 5
Thiamine, discovery of, 26
Thioridazine, 42
Thorazine, 41
Thymine, 127, 128, 129
Times, London, 74
Todaro, George, 169
Torok, Dr. Denes de, 146–147

Tranquilizers, 35–36, 42, 44, 225
    misuse of, 37
Transcendental meditation, 47
Trephining, 52–53, 71
    purpose of, 53
Tschermak, Erich von, 124
Tuberculosis, 21
Tuks, William, 34
Tumor angiogenesis factor (TAF), 175
Turner's disease, 142
Typhoid fever, 21
Typhus, 25

Unconscious processes, control of, 46–48
Union Carbide Corporation, 197
United Nations Scientific Committee on
    Effects of Atomic Radiation, 139
U.S. Agency for International Development, 83
U.S. Department of Agriculture, 25
U.S. Public Health Service, 43, 100
University of California at Berkeley, 167
University of California at Los Angeles
    (U.C.L.A.), 60, 66, 69, 78, 165, 167, 174
University of Chicago, 23, 103, 126, 153, 204, 208, 224
University of Cincinnati, 22
University College (London), 181
University of Hawaii, 204
University of Iowa, 12
University of London, 14
University of Miami, 121
University of Michigan, 152
University of Minnesota, 172, 173
University of Mississippi, 60
University of Pittsburgh, 22
University of San Diego, 227
University of Southern California, 44, 85, 99–100, 168, 186
University of Surrey, 67–68
University of Texas, 167
University of Vienna, 123
University of Virginia, 228
University of Wisconsin, 25, 170, 228–229
Uranium fission, 30
Urey, Harold, 121
Uterine cancer, 165

Vaccination, beginning of, 21–22
Vanderbilt University, 28, 83
Van Dyke, Dr. Palmer T., 88, 181
Vanilla, 7
Vein grafts, 99
Venereal disease, 23
Vesalius, Andreas, 57
Vibrio comma, 24
Vickery, Dr. Kenneth O. A., 195, 196
Victoria, Queen, 140
Vietnam War, 92
Vinblastin, 163

Vinca alkaloid drugs, 163
Vincristin, 163
Viruses, 114–115, 154, 206
  cancer and, 167–170
Vitalism, doctrine of, 111
Vitamin A, 26
Vitamin B₁, 26
Vitamin B₂ (riboflavin), 27
Vitamin B₁₂, 27, 185
Vitamin C, 25
Vitamin D, 25
Vitamin E, 26, 188
Vitamin K, 26–27
Vitamin supplements, 27
Vocational rehabilitation, government
  programs in, 95

Wald, George, 120–121
Wall Street Journal, The, 91
Wallace, Alfred, 112
Wallace, Dr. R. Keith, 47
Washington University, 128
Washkansky, Louis, 51–52
Water pollution, 166
Watson, Dr. James D., 127–131, 201, 214
Wayne State University, 212, 214
Weil, Dr. Max H., 85–86
Weissman, Dr. Gerald, 131

Wells, Horace, 58
Wied, Dr. George L., 66
Williams, Robert, 26
Williams, Roger, 26
Wilm's tumor, 163
Wilson's disease, 145
Winick, Dr. Charles, 12
Wisconsin Medical Society, 185
Witchcraft, 7–8
  pharmaceutical benefits, 8
  Salem hysteria, 8
World Health Organization, 181, 182
World War I, 92
World War II, 15, 77, 98, 149
Wright, Sewell, 126

X-ray technology, 76–77
X-rays, 82, 83, 100, 138, 145
  discovery of, 76, 160
XX chromosomes, 139
XYY syndrome, 142–144, 152

Y chromosome, 139, 216
Yeast cells, size of, 113
Yoga, 47
Yogi, Maharishi Mahesh, 47
Yohimbine, 8